BLAST OFF!

on
California
English Language Arts

Book 3

This book belongs to: _____

Buckle Down
Publishing

A Haights Cross Communications Company

Helping the schoolhouse meet the standards of the statehouse™

Acknowledgments

Six definitions and pronunciation key from *Scott, Foresman Beginning Dictionary* by E. L. Thorndike and Clarence L. Barnhart. Copyright © 1993, 1988, 1983, 1979, and 1976 by Scott, Foresman and Company. Reprinted by permission of Addison Wesley Educational Publishers, Inc.

"Frank E. Webner, pony express rider," photograph circa 1861, reprinted courtesy of the National Archives and Record Administration, Still Picture Branch, NWDNS-30-N-49-426.

Every effort has been made by the publisher to locate each owner of the copyrighted material reprinted in this publication and to secure the necessary permissions. If there are any questions regarding the use of these materials, the publisher will take appropriate corrective measures to acknowledge ownership in future publications.

ISBN 0-7836-2292-9

Catalog #BF CA3E 1   5 6 7 8 9 10

Editorial Director: John Hansen; Project Editor: Jill Foley; Editors: Jim Bartlett, Molly Hansen, John Ham, Karen Nichols; Production Editor: Michael Hankes; Production Director: Jennifer Booth; Production Supervisor: Ginny York; Art Director: Chris Wolf; Graphic Designer: Becky Evans, Contributing Illustrator: Judy Hierstein.

Cover: Images © 1996 PhotoDisc, Inc.

TABLE OF CONTENTS

Introduction

Do you like language arts? If you do, reading and writing are probably easy for you. You'll have fun reading the passages and doing the writing exercises in this book.

If you don't like language arts, it may be because reading and writing are difficult for you. If that's the case, don't give up! If you're willing to practice, you can count on becoming a better reader and writer than you are today. *Blast Off on California English Language Arts, Book 3*, will give you lots of language arts tips and practice, which will help you read and write the best you can. This book will help you take language arts tests, too.

So, go ahead, exercise your brain by reading and writing in this book. The more you practice, the better you'll get. And the better you get at reading and writing, the more fun you'll have doing them. Pretty soon, you'll be able to say, "I LOVE language arts!"

How to Use This Workbook

In *Blast Off*, you'll find lots and lots of reading passages. Some of them are made-up (**fiction**) stories, plays, or poems. Others are about real things and real people (**nonfiction**).

In Unit 1, you will learn how to use your "word power." You will learn how to **decode** (understand) some of the words that stop you when you're reading.

In Units 2 and 3, some of the lessons begin with a passage that will help you understand the tips that follow. These passages will give you some fun reading practice.

In Units 4 and 5, you will learn how to become a better writer. Soon you'll be writing your own passages for others to read.

The reading and writing practice you do now will help you when you take tests. You are likely to see several types of questions on language arts tests. You'll learn about them in this workbook.

By the time you've finished this book, you'll be something of a test "expert." You'll know just what kinds of questions to expect on any language arts test you take. But more important, this book will help you become a better reader and writer for the rest of your life.

UNIT 1

Words at Work

In many ways, understanding words is the same as solving a mystery. First, you gather clues about a word. Then you carefully study them. By the time you are finished, you probably know how to say the word. You may also know what it means.

In this unit, you'll learn about the clues to look for when you're trying to figure out a word. If you practice using these clues, you will become a better reader.

But that's not all! This unit will help you become a better writer, too. You may know what word you are trying to write, but if you can't spell it, your readers won't understand what you're trying to say. The word clues you use for reading can also help you with spelling.

What else will this unit do for you? It'll help you do your best on any language arts test you take. Sounds good, doesn't it?

Let's get started!

In This Unit
- *Building Words*
- *Spelling Tricks*
- *Taking Words Apart*
- *Word Play*
- *Word Power*

3

Building Words

Words come in parts, like building blocks. If you don't put the word parts together correctly, your words will fall apart.

One of your jobs as an editor is to catch spelling errors. Understanding word parts helps to improve your spelling. In this lesson, you'll learn how to build words, and you'll review a few other spelling tips.

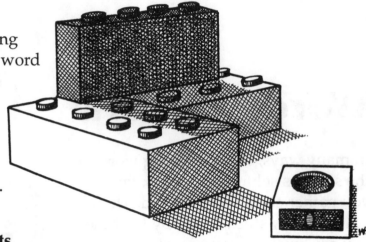

Tip 1 **Understand word parts.**

The first step in building words is understanding different word parts. The **base** (or root) of a word is usually the biggest part. In the word *handful*, the base word is *hand*. The **suffix** (the part that comes after the base word) *ful* means "full." So if you have a *handful* of gumballs, your *hand* is *full* of gumballs. (You'll learn more about suffixes later.)

A **prefix** is the word part that comes before the base word. In the word *midnight*, the prefix *mid* means "middle." So the word *midnight* means the "middle" of the "night."

Knowing how to spot word parts and understanding their meanings will help improve your spelling and boost your vocabulary.

Words with Suffixes

Word	Base Word	Suffix
cupful	cup	-ful
shorter	short	-er
deepest	deep	-est
beautiful	beauty	-ful
teacher	teach	-er
cleanest	clean	-est

Words with Prefixes

Word	Prefix	Base Word
unfold	un-	fold
redraw	re-	draw
prepare	pre-	pare
bicycle	bi-	cycle
misspell	mis-	spell
disobey	dis-	obey

Practice Activity 1: Building Words with Word Parts

Directions: Add the following word parts together.

1. tri + cycle = _____tricycle_____

2. thank + ful = _____

3. re + move = _____

4. en + joy = _____

5. loud + er = _____

Practice Activity 2: Prefixes

Directions: Read the following sentences. After each sentence, write a word that begins with a prefix and has the same meaning as the underlined words. Number 6 has been done for you.

6. Paul lost the race. He wanted to <u>run</u> it <u>again</u>.

   _____rerun_____

7. If you don't understand the story, <u>read</u> it <u>again</u>.

   _____

8. Shawna said that the story was <u>not true</u>.

   _____

9. Tiffany thought the rules of the game were <u>not fair</u>.

   _____

10. Did you <u>not understand</u> what I said?

   _____

Tip 2 Change *y* to *i*.

If a **consonant** comes right before the *y* at the end of a word, change the *y* to an *i* and add the suffix.

pretty + ness = pretti<u>ness</u>

If a **vowel** comes right before the *y*, do NOT change the *y* to an *i* before adding the suffix.

destroy + ed = destroy<u>ed</u>

Whenever the suffix begins with *i* (*-ing, -ion, -ible, -ist, -ish*), do NOT change the *y* to *i* before adding the suffix.

carry + ing = carry<u>ing</u>

Practice Activity 3: Changing *y* to *i*

Directions: Add the suffixes to each of the base words that follow. Change *y* to *i* when necessary.

11. beauty + ful = _____

12. fly + ing = _____

13. play + er = _____

14. lively + est = _____

15. steady + er = _____

16. easy + est = _____

17. pay + able = _____

18. skinny + er = _____

19. funny + est = _____

20. plenty + ful = _____

Practice Activity 4: Checking Your Spelling

Directions: Edit the following sentences by crossing out the misspelled word. Then write the correct spelling above it. Change *y* to *i* when necessary.

21. Spot enjoys *buriing* his puppy food in the backyard.

22. I felt so much *happyness* when I first discovered my neighbor's trampoline.

23. Nita *carryed* her picnic basket on top of her head.

24. Yesterday was Eric's *sixtyeth* birthday.

25. "*Lonelyness* is the worst feeling in the world," Marty said.

Building Words
Lesson 1 Review

Now you've got the hang of it! Here are the tips one more time:

- Understand word parts (know how to spot base words, suffixes, and prefixes).

- Before adding a suffix, change *y* to *i* if a consonant comes right before the *y*.

Spelling Tricks

Good spellers have a bag of tricks that they use to solve spelling problems. By the end of this lesson, your own bag of spelling tricks will be full of ways to make you an expert speller!

Tip 1 **When a vowel is followed by one or more consonants (except *r*), it usually makes a short-vowel sound.**

These are some examples of this rule:

hop   silk   address   rust   press   village   pup

1. Think of one more word that follows this rule. Write it on the following line.

_____

Tip 2 **When a vowel is followed by double consonants (like *tt*, *ss*, or *bb*), the vowel usually makes a short-vowel sound.**

These are some examples of this rule:

giggle   hobby   million   odd   ribbon   slippery

2. Think of one more word that follows this rule. Write it on the following line.

_____

Tip 3 **When a vowel is followed by two consonants and then *-le*, it usually makes a short-vowel sound.**

These are some examples of this rule:

cuddle   juggle   prickle   sprinkle   sparkle   waffle

3. Think of one more word that follows this rule. Write it on the following line.

_____

Tip 4 **When a vowel is followed by one consonant and then -*le*, it usually makes a long-vowel sound.**

These are some examples of this rule:

   a**ble**   cy**cle**   ma**ple**   sta**ble**   ta**ble**   ti**tle**

4. Think of one more word that follows this rule. Write it on the following line.

_____

Tip 5 **Remember word families.**

There are many groups of words that share similar spellings. These are called **word families**. When you learn a new word, try to think of another word that it is spelled like. This will help you remember how to spell when you are sounding out words in your head. Look at the following word families.

the "ight" family

bright   right

light   flight

the "oa" family

float   foam

boat   moan

Other word families include *ck, sh, rr, fr, ing, ai, ou,* and *st*.

Now it's your turn. In the space below, list some words in the "oo" family. (Example: *b<u>oo</u>k*)

Practice Activity: Spelling Patterns

Directions: In the table that follows, fill in each space with a word from the same word family as the example. Use the picture clues to help you.

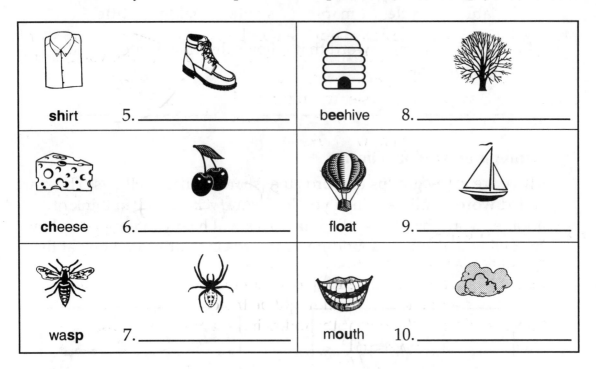

shirt	5. _____	**bee**hive	8. _____
cheese	6. _____	fl**oa**t	9. _____
wa**sp**	7. _____	m**ou**th	10. _____

Spelling Tricks
Lesson 2 Review

Now you have a full bag of spelling tricks to use when you're reading or writing. Here they are one more time:

- When a vowel is followed by one or more consonants (except *r*), it usually makes a short-vowel sound.

- When a vowel is followed by double consonants (like *tt*, *ss*, or *bb*), the vowel usually makes a short-vowel sound.

- When a vowel is followed by two consonants and then *-le*, it usually makes a short-vowel sound.

- When a vowel is followed by one consonant and then *-le*, it usually makes a long-vowel sound.

- Remember word families.

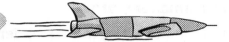

Taking Words Apart

In Lesson 1, you learned about the building blocks that make up words (such as base words, suffixes, and prefixes). In this lesson, you'll learn how to take words apart. Words like *extraordinary* become easier to understand and spell when you break them into parts. And, once you learn how to take words apart, you'll be an extraordinary speller!

Tip 1 **Separate words into sounds.**

Separate difficult words into sounds. The sounds that make up a word can come from one letter or several letters. An example of a one-letter sound might be the **consonant** *c* (*kuh*) or the **vowel** *a* (*ah*) in *call*. Look at the following examples of words that have been separated into sounds.

pal	p / a / l	cut	c / u / t
pale	p / a / l / e	cute	c / u / t / e

Look back at the words *pal*, *pale*, *cut*, and *cute*. When an *e* follows a consonant-vowel-consonant pattern (*pal*, *cut*) it makes the vowel say its name (*pale*, *cute*).

Examples of sounds that are made with several letters might be the letters in the **blended sound** of *br* in *bread* and the *ight* sound heard in the word *light*. Look at the following examples of words with blended sounds.

drip	dr / i / p	trap	tr / a / p
stamp	st / a / m / p	glass	gl / a / ss

When you come across a tricky sound, such as the *eigh* in *neighborhood*, remember other words with the same spelling. In this case, you might remember how the word *weigh* is spelled. If you can remember how to spell *weigh*, you can figure out the spelling of the word *neighborhood*.

Tip 2 **Separate compound words into smaller words.**

A **compound word** is a word made of two or more smaller words (such as *rowboat*). When writing a compound word, think about the smaller words that make up the whole word. This will make spelling easier.

Practice Activity 1: Taking Apart Compound Words

Directions: Look at the following examples of compound words. Then, write the smaller words that make up the compound words.

Example: watermelon = ___water + melon___

1. typewriter = _____

2. rattlesnake = _____

3. peppermint = _____

4. earthquake = _____

5. basketball = _____

6. farmhouse = _____

7. grasshopper = _____

8. meanwhile = _____

9. notebook = _____

10. waterproof = _____

Check Out the Spelling Log!

On page 147 of this workbook, you will find a spelling log. It provides a place to record difficult words and to practice spelling them. This will help you improve your spelling. Any time your teacher points out a misspelled word in your work, record the correct spelling in the log.

Tip 3 **Squeeze two words together to make contractions.**

To make a **contraction**, two words are squeezed together into one word and some of the letters are taken out. An apostrophe (') takes the place of the missing letters.

Look at the following examples of contractions:

can + not = **can't** (The apostrophe takes the place of the letters *no*.)

you + will = **you'll** (The apostrophe takes the place of the letters *wi*.)

they + have = **they've** (The apostrophe takes the place of the letters *ha*.)

it + is = **it's** (The apostrophe takes the place of the letter *i*.)

we + are = **we're** (The apostrophe takes the place of the letter *a*.)

Practice Activity 2: Making Contractions

Directions: Make the following words into contractions. You may look back at the examples to help you.

11. are + not = _____

12. he + will = _____

13. I + have = _____

14. she + is = _____

15. they + are = _____

16. they + will = _____

17. is + not = _____

18. will + not = _____

Practice Activity 3: Contractions in Sentences

Directions: Rewrite each of the following sentences. Combine the words in **bold** to form a contraction. Don't forget the apostrophe!

19. **I will** make a poster for my social studies project.

_____

20. **She would** like to go to Sierra National Forest.

_____

21. **You are** invited to Story Hour at the public library.

_____

22. **It is** fun to go fishing at Berry Creek.

_____

23. **You have** almost finished this Practice Activity.

_____

—————— **Taking Words Apart** ——————
Lesson 3 Review

Now you know about taking words apart to make spelling easier. Here are the tips one more time:

- Separate words into sounds.
- Separate compound words into smaller words.
- Squeeze two words together to make contractions.

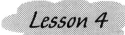 

Word Play

Is your mother's sister your *ant* or your *aunt*?

Did you *buy*, *by*, or *bye* a pack
of gum?

English has many words that
sound alike but have different
spellings and meanings. Words
such as *aunt* and *ant*, or *buy*, *by*,
and *bye*, are called **homophones**.

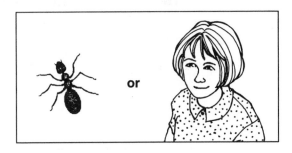

When you read, you often have to sound out new words. Sometimes
you know the meaning as soon as you say a word. But homophones
can be tricky. The same sound may have two or three different
meanings. This lesson will help you when you're not sure of a word.

Tip 1 Start by sounding out an unknown word.

If you don't know a word by sight, the first thing to do is to sound it
out. Let's pretend that you read the following sentence in a story:

"Joe was not happy when he saw a <u>flea</u> on his toothbrush."

You're not sure what *flea* means, so you sound it out.

The letters *f* and *l* together are a consonant blend. This means their
sounds are squished together. Easy enough: *f* and *l* say *fluh*.

The letters *e* and *a* together follow this rule about two vowels when
they are side by side: *when two vowels go walking, the first one does the
talking*.

1. What vowel sound does *ea* make in *flea*? _____

Okay, let's try it: *fl* plus long *e* sounds like *flee*. But there's more than
one word with the same *flee* sound. So you still may not be sure of
what *flea* means. What's your next step?

Tip 2 **Use a dictionary to look up the meanings of homophones.**

See how the word is spelled in the reading passage. Then find that word in the dictionary.

Here's one dictionary's definition of the word *flea*:

> **flea:** a small, wingless insect

2. Look up *flea* in your own dictionary. Write the meaning on the following lines:

_____

_____

Now you're ready for the next step.

Tip 3 **Plug in the definition in place of the unknown word.**

Reread the sentence that contains the word *flea*:

> "Joe was not happy when he saw a <u>flea</u> on his toothbrush."

Now plug in the definition in place of the word. Then read the sentence to yourself:

3. "Joe was not happy when he saw a _____ on his toothbrush."

Does your new sentence make sense?

Tip 4 **Look for clues in the passage.**

If you read a word that you don't know, you will probably find all sorts of clues to the word's meaning in the story or passage.

Synonyms

Sometimes the story will have other words with nearly the same meaning as the word you are trying to figure out. Words with nearly the same meaning are called **synonyms**.

Read the following passage, then answer Numbers 4 and 5.

> The old man was very poor. Each day he would <u>labor</u> in his field until he was so tired that he could barely move. As the sun set, the old man would stop his hard work. Then he would throw his hoe over his shoulder and slowly walk home to his small cottage.

4. Underline any words or phrases in the passage that you think might be similar in meaning to the word *labor*.

5. Which of the following words is a synonym for the word *labor*?
   A. work   C. wander
   B. laugh   D. daydream

Antonyms

Sometimes the passage will give you clues to the opposite meanings of a word. Words with opposite meanings are called **antonyms**. If you can figure out a word's opposite, you can make a good guess about its meaning. Read the following passage, then answer Numbers 6 and 7.

> Although Carmen was usually <u>prompt</u> for her music lesson, today she was 10 minutes late.

6. Underline any words in the sentence that you think might have the opposite meaning of *prompt*.

7. Which of the following is the best antonym for the word *prompt*?
   A. sad   C. puzzled
   B. late   D. unhappy

Other clues

Some clues are not as easy to find. Read the following passage, then answer Number 8.

> Martin sat with his seat belt fastened. He looked out the small window of the airplane and wished it would move. He had been sitting on the plane for nearly 20 minutes, and he was <u>anxious</u> to take off.

8. What is the meaning of the word *anxious* as it is used in the passage?
   A. eager
   B. afraid
   C. unready
   D. promised

Tip 5 **On a test, plug in the answer choices.**

When you take most language arts tests, you won't be able to use a dictionary. But that's okay. The answer will always be right there in front of you in the answer choices!

If a question asks about the meaning of a word, plug in each answer choice. This works for homophones and other words, too. (You'll learn more tips about plugging in answer choices later.)

Decide which answer choice makes the most sense in the sentence. The word that makes the most sense is the correct answer. It's that simple!

Here's a passage for practice. Read the passage and the questions that follow it. Then circle the letter of each correct answer choice.

> The bus door opened with a *whoosh*. Jordy got on behind a white-haired man and took a seat next to a window.
> "Just a minute, young fella," the driver said to him. "You can't ride this bus without paying the <u>fare</u>."
> Oh, no! Jordy had been so worried about catching the <u>right</u> bus that he'd forgotten his money. What could he do now?

9. In the passage above, what does the word *fare* mean?
   A. same thing for everyone
   B. money charged to ride
   C. favor done for someone
   D. a kind of outdoor party

Which choice makes the most sense to you? Even if you've never ridden on a bus, you probably know the answer. A person who rides a bus has to pay a *fare* (an amount of money). In fact, the driver uses the word *paying* when he says, "You can't ride this bus without *paying* the fare."

Try another question like the last one.

10. In this passage, what does the word *right* mean?
    A. large   C. correct
    B. not the left   D. use a pencil

Practice Activity: Homophones

Directions: The following list contains some homophones you may know. They are used correctly in sentences. Fill in the missing homophones.

by	The weather is fairly warm **by** June.
bye	Say good-**bye** to winter weather.

11. _____   Let's rush out to _____ swimsuits.

---

12. _____   The tree was _____ after its leaves fell.
    bear   The **bear** stood on its hind legs and roared.

---

    dear   Jennifer's pets are very **dear** to her.

13. _____   Her favorite is a pet _____ named Bambi.

---

    hear   Did you **hear** the news?
    here   A bad storm will soon be **here**.

---

    know   I **know** a secret you don't know.

14. _____   _____, you may not go to the movies.

---

    road   Did Dorothy walk down the yellow brick **road**?
    rode   I'm pretty sure she **rode** her bike.

Tip 6 **Watch out for words that are spelled alike but have different meanings!**

Homographs are words that are spelled exactly alike, but have different meanings. Look at the following examples:

> April ate a *bowl* of cereal.
> Pedro likes to *bowl*.

> *Close* your eyes and stick out your tongue.
> The hurricane is *close*.

> A *tear* ran down Mike's cheek.
> *Tear* up that secret note!

> The *wind* was powerful.
> *Wind* up my yo-yo, please.

15. How is the word *bow* different in these two phrases?

     the *bow* of a ship   a *bow* and arrow

     _____

     _____

Word Play
Lesson 4 Review

When answering questions about homophones, synonyms, antonyms, and homographs, remember the following tips:

- Start by sounding out an unknown word.
- Use a dictionary to look up the meanings of homophones.
- Plug in the definition in place of the unknown word.
- Look for clues in the passage.
- On a test, plug in the answer choices.
- Watch out for words that are spelled alike but have different meanings.

Lesson 5

Word Power

Read the following passage. It will help you learn the tips in this lesson.

Sherlock Holmes and the Case of the Wheediddle
by Sandy Shaw

Sherlock Holmes put his violin back in its case. He stared once again at the note that had been slipped under his door. It was very, very strange. The writer had used many words that Sherlock and his partner, Dr. Watson, did not know. Holmes would have to look for clues to understand the note.

> **Daab** Mr. Holmes,
>
> Can we meet at 8 **o'grock**? Wait for me. I hope I'm not **lorgh**. Sometimes I forget to wind my **wheediddle** and it stops. Then I don't know what time it is. I'll meet you at the **bongle** of Baker Street and 10th Avenue. Try not to be **lorgh**!
>
> Very truly **yongs**,
> Hobart Tinwhistle

"Well," said Sherlock, "**Daab** must mean *Dear* since most letters begin with that word.

"And **o'grock** could mean *o'clock*, since it is matched with the number 8."

The great detective continued to study the letter. "**Wheediddle** must mean *watch* or *clock*, since the writer says that his wheediddle stops when he doesn't wind it—and then he doesn't know what time it is.

"**Lorgh** must mean *late*. He hopes he won't be late if his watch stops. Then, later in the note, he tells *me* not to be **lorgh**. Yes, I am certain that **lorgh** means *late*," Sherlock said to himself. "**Bongle** must mean *corner*, since Baker Street crosses 10th Avenue.

"And, finally," the detective said, "**yongs** must mean *yours*. Mr. Tinwhistle is probably trying to close his letter with 'Very truly yours.' "

"Dr. Watson!" Sherlock called excitedly. "Come. Grab your coat and hat. We must meet a certain Mr. Tinwhistle at the corner of Baker Street and 10th Avenue at 8 o'clock. And," he added, "we must not be 'lorgh'!" ❖

Become a Word Detective

Did you know there are more than a million words in the English language? This means that *all of us*—third-graders, teachers, store workers, authors, even the people who write dictionaries—sometimes see words we don't know.

When you see a new word that makes no sense, don't give up. Be a detective, just like Sherlock Holmes. First, try to sound out the beginning, middle, and end of the word. Does it make sense to you? If not, look for clues to help you figure out the word. Usually, you will be able to find them in the reading passage. You just have to know what to look for. This lesson will show you how to become a word detective.

Tip 1 **Don't stop reading when you come to a word you don't know.**

The best way to understand a new word is to use other words you already know to help you. So don't stop reading just because you don't know a word. Say it to yourself, then go right on reading.

Sometimes other words in the passage will give clues to the meaning of the new word. Often these words are found close together—or even in the same sentence. Look at these examples:

> 1) In this area, we can find *gabbro*, a dark, heavy rock.

> 2) She looked in her coin purse and found one *dinar*.

> 3) For *recreation*, he enjoys swimming and baseball.

1. What is *gabbro*?

   _____

2. What is a *dinar*?

   _____

3. What is the meaning of *recreation*?

_____

4. Look back at Mr. Tinwhistle's letter on page 21. Underline details that give clues to the meaning of the word *wheediddle*.

Tip 2 **Go back to the passage, find the unknown word, and read the words that come before and after it.**

When a question on a reading test asks you about the meaning of a word or a **phrase** (a group of words), first go back to the passage and find it. Don't just try to guess its meaning without looking.

Once you find the word, put your finger on it. Read the words that come before and after it in the sentence. The other words in a sentence often help you understand the unknown word.

Tip 3 **Read the sentences around the unknown word.**

If you still don't understand the word, read the whole paragraph. While reading, look carefully for clues that will help you figure out the meaning. Once you've found all the clues you can, make your best guess.

Read the following paragraph. It tells about an imaginary thing called a *grundle*. Try to figure out what a *grundle* is.

A grundle is beautiful and very useful. A full-grown grundle is big enough to make shade in the summer. In the spring, its blossoms have a wonderful smell. A grundle has strong branches that hold a lot of juicy fruit.

5. What do you know about a *grundle* from reading the paragraph?

_____

_____

6. Based on the paragraph, what is a *grundle*?
   A. a kind of tree   C. a kind of flower
   B. a kind of weed   D. a kind of vegetable

Tip 4 Try each answer choice in place of the unknown word.

Plugging in the answer choices will help you make sure you have the right answer.

When you are asked the meaning of a word, find the sentence in the passage. Replace the unknown word with each answer choice, one at a time. The answer that makes the most sense is probably correct.

Read the following paragraph.

> I think most people called her Peggy the Pumpkin Princess. Remember, now, that was a long time ago. To the best of my <u>recollection</u>, she never called herself by that name. In fact, she hated pumpkins—and her real name was Agnes!

Read Number 7, but don't answer it yet.

7. What is the meaning of the word *recollection*?
   A. eyesight   C. sense of touch
   B. memory   D. sense of smell

First, find the sentence that contains the word *recollection*.

> To the best of my <u>recollection</u>, she never called herself by that name.

Then try each answer choice in place of the word *recollection* in the sentence.

   A. To the best of my <u>eyesight</u>, she never called herself by that name.
   B. To the best of my <u>memory</u>, she never called herself by that name.
   C. To the best of my <u>sense of touch</u>, she never called herself by that name.
   D. To the best of my <u>sense of smell</u>, she never called herself by that name.

Which answer choice makes the most sense?

Tip 5 **A dictionary will help you learn new words.**

If you're still stuck, a dictionary is a great place to learn about new words. It tells about words and their meanings. It also tells how words are spelled and pronounced. Sometimes a dictionary will show you how the word is used in a sentence.

Words in a dictionary are listed in alphabetical order. A page in a dictionary looks something like this:

kilowatt ∣ knapsack   323

a hat	**i** it	**oi** oil	**ch** child		**a** in about
ā age	**ī** ice	**ou** out	**ng** long		**e** in taken
ä far	**o** hot	**u** cup	**sh** she	**ə =**	**i** in pencil
e let	**ō** open	**u̇** put	**th** thin		**o** in lemon
ē equal	**ô** order	**ü** rule	**ᴛʜ** then		**u** in circus
ėr term			**zh** measure		

kil o watt (kil′ə wot′), a unit for measuring electric power equal to 1000 watts. *noun.*

kilt (kilt), a pleated skirt, reaching to the knees, worn by men in parts of Scotland. *noun.*

ki mo no (kə mō′nə), **1** a loose outer garment held in place by a sash, worn by both men and women in Japan. **2** a woman's loose dressing gown. *noun, plural* **ki mo nos.**

kin (kin), **1** family or relatives; kindred: *All our kin came to the family reunion.* **2** family relationship: *What kin is she to you?* **3** related: *Your cousin is also kin to me.* 1, 2 *noun,* 3 *adjective.*
next of kin, nearest living relative.

kind¹ (kīnd), **1** friendly; doing good rather than harm: *A kind person tries to help others. Sharing your lunch was a kind thing to do.* **2** gentle: *Be kind to animals. adjective.*

kind² (kīnd), **1** sort; type: *I like many kinds of food. A kilt is a kind of skirt.* **2** natural group: *The wolf hunted in a pack with others of its kind. noun.*
of a kind, of the same sort: *The cakes were all of a kind—chocolate.*

8. Who would most likely wear a *kimono*?

    A. Someone from Japan

    B. Someone from Scotland

    C. Someone who fixes cars

    D. Someone who exercises at the gym

You will learn more about using a dictionary in Lesson 21.

Tip 6 **Think about how words relate to one another.**

There are many ways to say the same thing. Some words are **general** (such as *animal* or *mammal*) and some words are **specific** (such as *dog* or *dalmation*). Look at the following graphic organizer. It shows how these words relate to one another.

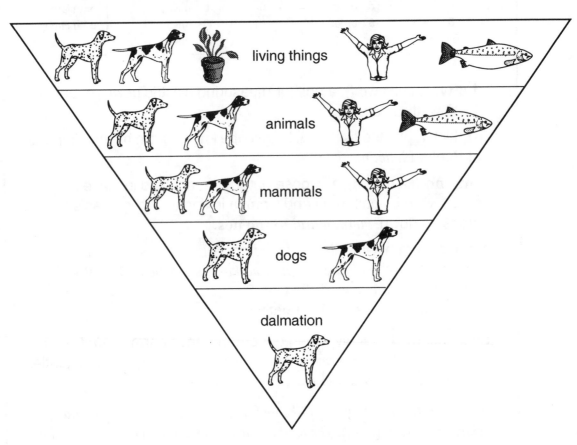

9. According to the diagram, what are two living things that are not mammals?

    A. plants and people

    B. plants and fish

    C. people and dogs

    D. fish and dogs

Put the following words in order from general to specific. The most general word in each example has been filled in for you.

grapes   fruit   food   white grapes

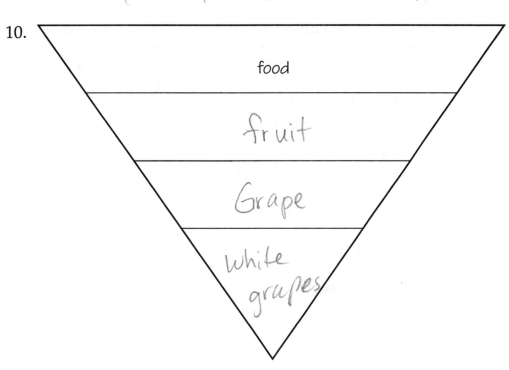

10.

food

fruit

Grape

White grapes

sports   after-school activities   soccer   team sports

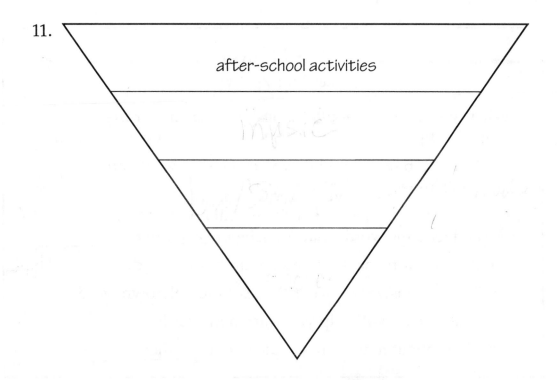

11.

after-school activities

music

12. Which of the following is most general?

    A. oceans on Earth   C. bodies of water

    B. rivers and streams   D. creeks and ponds

13. Which of the following is in order from general to specific?

A.
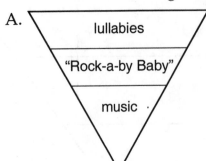

C.
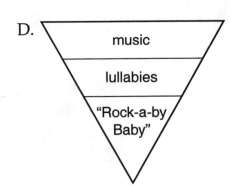

B.
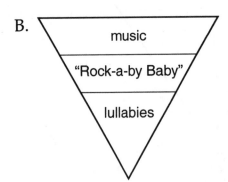

D.

Word Power
Lesson 5 Review

When answering vocabulary questions, remember the following tips:

- Don't stop reading when you come to a word you don't know.

- Go back to the passage, find the unknown word, and read the words that come before and after it.

- Read the sentences around the unknown word.

- Try each answer choice in place of the unknown word.

- A dictionary will help you learn new words.

- Think about how words relate to one another.

Practice Passage

Directions: Read the passage and answer the questions that follow.

The First Brothers of Flight
by Ted Remington

1   About 100 years before the Wright brothers were born, Jacques (*Zhock*) and Joseph Montgolfier (Mahn-GAHL-fee-ay) lived in a little town not far from Paris, France. One day, Joseph threw a paper bag into a fire. Before it could burn, the bag floated up the chimney. This gave the men an idea.

2   The hot air <u>captured</u> inside the bag must be lighter than the cool air around it, they thought. That would make the bag rise. To test their idea, they made a balloon and filled it with hot air. It rose off the ground as the paper bag had. Their idea had been right!

3   The brothers made larger and larger balloons. They wanted to make a balloon big enough to carry a person into the sky. If their plan worked, Jacques and Joseph's balloon would be the world's first flying machine.

4   The brothers finally made a balloon big enough to carry two people. But what if their balloon fell? The passengers could be hurt—or worse. They decided to send up animals instead of people. The very first hot air balloon passengers were a goat, a duck, and a rooster. After a smooth flight, the animals landed in a treetop two miles away. The brothers decided it was time to send a person <u>aloft</u>.

5   On November 21, 1783, a great crowd watched the men fill their giant balloon. At the sound of a cannon, the brothers untied the ropes that held the balloon to the ground. Two young Frenchmen were on board, but they were *not* the Montgolfier brothers.

6   Finally, the blue and gold balloon rose high into the sky. It <u>glided</u> silently and <u>calmly</u> over the rooftops of Paris, far above the cheering people. After floating five miles, the brave <u>passengers</u> landed gently on the ground. The trip had lasted 20 minutes.

7   Thanks to Jacques and Joseph Montgolfier, a whole new way of traveling became possible. The world would never be the same. ❖

Sample Vocabulary Questions

1. In paragraph 2, what does *captured* mean?
   A. stolen
   B. falling
   C. trapped
   D. whistling

2. In paragraph 4, the writer says, ". . . it was time to send a person *aloft*." This means it was time to send a person
   A. to Paris.
   B. to space.
   C. up into the sky.
   D. to the nearest farm.

3. In paragraph 6, the writer says that the balloon *glided*. This means that the balloon
   A. flew smoothly.
   B. bounced hard.
   C. jerked to a stop.
   D. roared loudly.

4. To do something *calmly* is to do it
   A. nervously.
   B. peacefully and quietly.
   C. with quick movements.
   D. angrily and loudly.

5. Read the following definition of the word *passenger*:

   pas•sen•ger (PASS-en-jer), n. 1. a person traveling in a car, train, or airplane, especially one who is not the driver

   In paragraph 6, what does the word *passengers* mean?
   A. goats
   B. riders
   C. animals
   D. villagers

6. Which of the following lists is in order from general to specific?
   A. things that float, balloons, hot air balloons
   B. balloons, hot air balloons, things that float
   C. balloons, things that float, hot air balloons
   D. hot air balloons, balloons, things that float

Additional Practice Questions

7. What is this passage mainly about?
   A. burning paper bags
   B. early French airplanes
   C. balloon races across France
   D. the Montgolfiers' invention

8. The first balloon to carry people traveled how many miles?
   A. three
   B. four
   C. five
   D. six

9. This passage is an example of
   A. fiction
   B. poetry
   C. drama
   D. nonfiction

Understanding What You Read

Imagine that your parents have just given you the big picture: *WE'RE MOVING!*

Once you arrive in your new neighborhood, you start to get the details. Your room is bigger than you thought it would be. There's a park down the street with the best play equipment you've ever seen. And within a few days, you meet three kids your age. Maybe moving wasn't such a bad idea after all.

Picking up a new book is a little like moving to a new home. You start to get the "big picture," or **main idea**, when you first look at the cover and the title. As you read, you begin to get the details (and the main idea becomes clearer, too).

In this unit, you will learn ways to make sure you understand the main idea, details, and other important parts of a passage.

In This Unit
- ◆ *What's It All About?*
- ◆ *Problems and Predictions*
- ◆ *Reading Strategies*
- ◆ *A Treasure Map to Knowledge*
- ◆ *Dealing with Directions*

What's It All About?

Read the following passage. It will help you learn the tips in this lesson.

The Pony Express
by Chandler Wobble

In the mid 1800s, there were only two ways to get to California. One way was to sail around the tip of South America. This took a long time. Another way was to cross mountains and deserts on foot and in wagons. Either way, it was a hard and dangerous trip. But, thousands of people moved west anyway. California grew quickly and became a state in 1850.

Because California was far from the rest of the United States, mail service was very slow. It could take months for letters to be delivered. Nobody wanted to wait that long for news about their friends and families far away.

A man named William H. Russell ran a company that carried goods and passengers by wagon and stagecoach. In 1860, he hired a group of young men to ride fast horses from St. Joseph, Missouri, to Sacramento, California. Each rider would carry the mail for about 80 miles, stopping at a relay station every 10 to 15

Eight Pony Express riders were on the job at any one time. There were also about 400 other Pony Express employees, including station keepers.

miles to get a fresh horse. When he reached his final stop (called a home station), he would give the mail to another rider, who would carry it 80 miles to the next home station. (It was like a relay race.)

This way, the mail could get to and from California much faster. The new mail service was called the Pony Express.

The Pony Express wanted riders who did not have families because the job was so dangerous. The young men rode alone across Indian lands. It was a difficult job, but the mail almost always got through. It took the riders only eight or ten days to go from St. Joseph to Sacramento, instead of many weeks.

After 18 months, telegraph wires finally reached California, making it easier to send and receive messages. The Pony Express went out of business. It has been famous ever since as a colorful part of the history of the Old West. ❖

The Most Important Idea

Everything you read—whether it's a story, a poem, or even a math book—tells you something. That "something" is called the **main idea**. It's what the passage is *mostly* about. Some stories have many important ideas, but there is only one *most* important idea.

Here are some of the important ideas in "The Pony Express":

- The trip west to California was hard and dangerous.
- William H. Russell started a service that carried the mail to and from California.
- Riding for the Pony Express could be a dangerous job.
- The Pony Express ran for only about 18 months.

There is only one *main* idea in the whole story about the Pony Express. The main idea isn't given in a single sentence. You have to put together the details to figure it out.

1. What is the most important idea of the passage?
   A. Pony Express relay stations were about 15 miles apart.
   B. It took a long time to sail around the tip of South America.
   C. The Pony Express cut the time for mail service to and from California.
   D. William H. Russell ran a company that carried goods and passengers by wagon.

2. Go back to the story and underline details that tell about the main idea.

Tip 1 **Look for a sentence that tells the main idea.**

Sometimes a writer will come right out and tell you the main idea in a sentence.

> Spider webs are interesting and unusual things. Most spider webs are sticky because they are used to trap prey. But how do spiders walk on the webs without getting stuck? They have oily feet that slip and slide easily over the silk. Should a spider fall backward onto its own web, it will stick there like any other creature. Aargh!
>
> There is a spider in Europe that spins a web so tiny it's hard to see. It would barely cover a postage stamp.
>
> If you went to India, however, you might see something quite the opposite of such a tiny web. One Indian spider builds a web so big that it could cover half your classroom.
>
> The **water spider**, as you might guess from its name, doesn't mind the water. But before crawling in, it moves its bell-shaped web through the water to collect air bubbles. When it has enough air bubbles, the spider heads below in its own little diving bell to look for food. ❖

3. Underline the sentence that tells the main idea of the passage.

4. What is the first paragraph mainly about?
   A. the way spiders walk on their sticky webs
   B. the tiny web made by a spider from Europe
   C. the huge web made by an Indian spider
   D. the way the water spider uses its web to collect air bubbles

5. What is the last paragraph mainly about?
   A. the way spiders walk on their sticky webs
   B. the tiny web made by a spider from Europe
   C. the huge web made by an Indian spider
   D. the way the water spider uses its web to collect air bubbles

Tip 2 **Look for details that support the main idea.**

Supporting details give important information about the main idea. You could say that they help to "hold up" the main idea. In the paragraph about spider webs, the main idea is that webs are interesting and unusual. The details tell about interesting and unusual webs.

The next paragraph is from a book about Eleanor Roosevelt. She was a writer, a United Nations delegate, and the wife of President Franklin D. Roosevelt. It tells what Eleanor and her family saw in London when she was a child.

> Sometimes the people looked strange and exciting. They saw men from Scotland who wore plaid skirts, which Eleanor's father said were called *kilts*. They saw women from India dressed in yards and yards of beautiful cloth, which her mother said were called *saris*. In one large building they saw some English judges who wore long black robes and long white wigs that reached to their shoulders.

—from *Eleanor Roosevelt: Fighter for Social Justice* by Ann Weil

6. What is the main idea of the paragraph?
   A. Some people looked strange and exciting to Eleanor.
   B. Men from Scotland wore plaid skirts called *kilts*.
   C. Women wore yards of beautiful cloth called *saris*.
   D. English judges wore long black robes and white wigs.

7. Look back at the paragraph about Eleanor Roosevelt. Circle two details that support the main idea.

Tip 3 **Put the main idea into your own words.**

Sometimes a writer just hints at the main idea. If you can't find a main idea sentence, try the following:

- Look for important details in the passage.
- Decide how the details work together.
- In your own words, tell how the details are connected.

Your sentence should tell how the important ideas work together. The way they work together is what the passage is *mostly* about.

Read the following paragraph, then answer Numbers 8 through 11.

Freddy Dissel had two problems. One was his older brother, Mike. The other was his younger sister, Ellen. Freddy thought a lot about being the one in the middle. But there was nothing he could do about it. He felt like the peanut butter part of a sandwich, squeezed between Mike and Ellen.

—from *The One in the Middle Is the Green Kangaroo* by Judy Blume

8. What are Freddy Dissel's two problems?

_____

9. What does Freddy think about?

_____

10. How does Freddy feel?

_____

11. Which sentence best tells about the paragraph?
    A. Freddy has an older brother, Mike.
    B. Freddy has a younger sister, Ellen.
    C. Freddy doesn't like being the middle child.
    D. Freddy doesn't like peanut butter sandwiches.

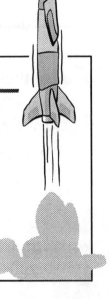

What's It All About?
Lesson 6 Review

When answering main idea questions, remember the following tips:

- Look for a sentence that tells the main idea.
- Look for details that support the main idea.
- Put the main idea into your own words.

Practice Passage

Directions: Read the passage and answer the questions that follow.

Silent Music

by Ted Remington and Jim Bartlett

Ludwig van Beethoven was one of history's greatest musicians. He played his first public concert when he was seven years old. He wrote many famous pieces of music. His works are still being played today. What makes Beethoven most unusual is that he wrote much of his greatest music after he lost his hearing.

Ludwig van Beethoven

Before he was 30 years old, Beethoven began to fear that he was going deaf. He was right. Soon, he couldn't hear a thing. It's hard to imagine a greater loss to a musician than the loss of one's hearing. Beethoven was deeply hurt. He had been one of the best piano players in all of Europe, but his skills had <u>faded</u> with his hearing. How could he play and write music if he could not hear?

Even though he was deaf, Beethoven did not feel as though his life's work was finished. Then, he realized something. He could still "see" the sound of music in his mind. By imagining the music, he could write down the notes and play them as he had done before. The joy of creating made him feel useful again.

One of Beethoven's most famous works is his Ninth Symphony. Hundreds of people came to hear it for the first time. When it was over, they clapped and cheered. Beethoven didn't know the crowd was cheering until he turned around and saw them. He had created a great work, but he never heard it. ❖

Sample Main Idea Questions

1. What is the main idea of "Silent Music"?
   A. Musicians cannot work if they lose their hearing.
   B. Beethoven wrote great music even though he was deaf.
   C. Beethoven's Ninth Symphony is one of his greatest works.
   D. Beethoven was one of the greatest piano players in Europe.

2. What is the main idea of the last paragraph of "Silent Music"?
   A. Beethoven created many masterpieces of music.
   B. Beethoven wrote great music before he was 30 years old.
   C. Beethoven could not hear his own music or the cheering crowd.
   D. Beethoven's Ninth Symphony was the last symphony he wrote.

3. Which detail from the passage supports the idea that deafness made Beethoven feel useless?
   A. Beethoven was deeply hurt.
   B. His music is still being performed today.
   C. A large crowd came to hear his Ninth Symphony.
   D. He played his first concert when he was seven years old.

Additional Practice Questions

4. In the second paragraph of the passage, what does the word *faded* mean?
   A. gotten better
   B. taken over
   C. gone away
   D. become less colorful

5. Why did the authors write "Silent Music"?
   A. to tell a funny story
   B. to show how to play the piano
   C. to make people want to visit Europe
   D. to tell about an interesting person from history

Lesson 7

Problems and Predictions

Read the following passage. It will help you learn the tips in this lesson.

from

What's Your Problem, Kid?
by Julie Render

"Dad! Come quick!" Rufus called from under his covers. No answer.

He shuddered. *Something is in my closet*, he thought.

"Dad!" he tried again. But again, the house was silent.

Two red lights stared at him. They had to be monster eyes. His teeth chattered at the thought.

Rufus tried to hold his shaking body still. "There's no such thing as monsters," he said. "There's no such thing as monsters. And there are no eyes in my closet."

When he was finally calm, Rufus quietly climbed out of bed. He tiptoed closer to his closet, sure that the red lights would turn out to be a teddy bear's eyes or the shiny red buttons on his cowboy shirt. But they might be monster eyes. It was hard to tell. He would have to turn on the light.

Rufus walked to the light switch by the doorway, feeling braver now that he was taking action. He reached out with his left hand and flipped the switch.

"Hey! Turn that off," a growly voice said. "You're waking me up."

Rufus froze, his hand still on the switch. It was a monster! And it was in his closet!

"DAD, come HELP me!" Rufus screamed.

"Rufus," his dad called from the next room. "Please be quiet. You might wake the monster in your closet." ❖

Almost every story includes some kind of problem. You will understand the story better if you think about what the problems are and how the characters solve them.

When you understand the characters in a story, you can make **predictions** (guesses) about how they will solve their problems and what they will do next.

Tip 1 **Find the main problem in the story.**

The characters in made-up stories always face at least one problem. A lot of real-life stories have problems in them, too. Sometimes, the problem is stated in one sentence. Other times, you have to put the details together to figure out what it is.

1. What is Rufus's main problem?

    _____

    _____

    _____

Tip 2 **Look for ways the characters try to solve the main problem.**

In most stories, the main character tries to solve the problem. In this story, Rufus tries two solutions. Look back at the story to find them.

2. What is the first solution Rufus tries?
    A. He gets out of bed.
    B. He calls for his dad.
    C. He tries to hold his shaking body still.
    D. He tells himself there's no such thing as monsters.

Rufus's first solution doesn't work. He has to try something else.

3. What does Rufus do when he gets out of bed?

    _____

Look Into the Future

Sometimes you can guess what is going to happen later in the story. You may not always guess right, but it's fun to try.

Tip 3 **Predict (make a good guess about) what will happen next in the story.**

Use clues from the story, the title, the pictures, and things you have learned in your own life, to figure out what will happen next.

Read each paragraph and predict what will happen next.

> Leon and Mimi finished spooning a batch of chocolate chip cookies onto a cookie sheet. After putting their cookies into a hot oven, they rushed outside to play for 10 minutes while the cookies baked.

4. Predict what will happen next.

   _____

   _____

   _____

> They laughed and played for 25 minutes before Mimi suddenly remembered the cookies. When they looked up, they saw clouds of smoke rolling from the kitchen window.

5. Was your prediction for Number 4 correct?   ❏ Yes   ❏ No

6. Predict what Leon and Mimi will do now.

   _____

   _____

   _____

Sometimes, your predictions might have to change as the story goes on. You might learn something new about a character that could change the story.

Olivia decided to take a shortcut through Mr. Johnson's pasture. She had forgotten about Mr. Johnson's large bull.

7. Predict what will happen next.

_____

_____

The large animal pawed the ground, then lowered its head and began to chase the girl. Running as fast as she could, Olivia looked up and saw a large oak tree near the pasture's edge.

8. Was your prediction for Number 7 correct?   ❏ Yes   ❏ No

9. Predict what Olivia will do now.

_____

_____

10. How would your prediction in Number 9 be different if Olivia suddenly remembered that she could make herself invisible?

_____

_____

Problems and Predictions
Lesson 7 Review

- Find the main problem in the story.
- Look for ways the characters try to solve the main problem.
- Predict (make a good guess about) what will happen next in the story.

Practice Passage

Directions: Read the passage and answer the questions that follow.

Grandpa's Kite
by Brian O'Sullivan

When I was eight, Mom and I moved from San Diego to Bakersfield. The good part was that my grandparents lived in Bakersfield. And the bad part? You guessed it. I was about to be "the new kid" in school.

I remember the morning Grandpa drove me to my new school for the first time. I was so scared, my stomach was doing flips. Would my teacher be nice? Would I make friends? Would everyone be ahead of me in math? I could hardly pay attention to Grandpa.

On the way, Grandpa asked, "Did I ever tell you about the first time I flew a kite, Brian?"

I shook my head.

"When I was a little kid—a couple years younger than you are now—my father told me we were going to fly a kite the next day. I was never more scared in my life!"

"Why would you be scared to fly a kite, Grandpa?"

"My dad was a pilot, so I figured a kite must be sort of like an airplane. I thought you had to ride on it to fly it."

"That's pretty funny, Grandpa!"

"Maybe so," Grandpa said, "but that's what I thought. I told my dad I didn't know how to fly a kite. I asked if he'd fly it with me."

"What did your dad say?" I asked.

"He said, 'Son, it's easy to fly a kite. Anyone can do it. Don't worry, I'll help you get the kite up in the air. Then you can fly it all by yourself.' What do you suppose I was thinking about all that night?" Grandpa asked.

"What it would be like to fly a kite?" I asked.

"No, I kept hoping it would rain! But when morning came, it was bright and sunny."

"Then what happened?" I asked.

"The next day, my dad brought out a big piece of paper that was stretched tight over some sticks. It had a long string tied to it. I was really confused then," Grandpa said. "I asked my dad, 'How am I supposed to ride on that little thing?' "

"What did he say?" I asked.

Grandpa laughed at the memory. "My dad was really surprised by what I had asked. I know he was trying hard not to laugh.

"Well, we went to a great big park. Dad showed me how to fly a kite, all right! Boy, did I feel silly when I found out that you fly a kite while you stand on the ground! Because I didn't know what a kite was, I had imagined it to be something scary. Flying a kite turned out to be safe and a lot of fun."

So, why is he telling me this now? I wondered.

The car pulled up in front of my school, and Grandpa opened the door to let me out.

"Say, Brian," he said. "When you walk in the door of your new class, just remember what I told you about the kite, okay?"

"Sure, Grandpa," I said. "Thanks for the ride. And thanks for telling me the story." I slipped my arms through the straps of my backpack and walked up the sidewalk to my new school.

Grandpa waved as he drove away.

Now what was that all about? I wondered.

But as I walked through the door, I felt ready for anything. ❖

Sample Problems and Predictions Questions

1. What is Brian's main problem in the story?

    A. He has never flown a kite before.

    B. He doesn't want to move to Bakersfield.

    C. He cannot hear what his grandpa is saying.

    D. He is nervous on his first day at a new school.

2. How does Grandpa help Brian solve his problem?

    A. He laughs at him.

    B. He tells him a story.

    C. He buys him a kite.

    D. He helps him put his backpack on.

3. At the end of the passage, Brian says, "I felt ready for anything." What does he mean?

  A. He wants to fly a kite with Grandpa after school.

  B. He is no longer afraid of being the new kid at school.

  C. He has decided to become a pilot when he grows up.

  D. He knows that he will be ahead of the class in math.

4. On his first day at the new school, Brian most likely will

  A. cry outside the doorway to his classroom.

  B. ask the principal if he can leave right away.

  C. get angry with everyone and start an argument.

  D. do his best to make friends and get to know people.

Additional Practice Questions

5. Which word best tells about Brian's grandpa?

  A. kind

  B. angry

  C. scared

  D. curious

6. Which of the following happens last in the story?

  A. Grandpa waves at Brian.

  B. Grandpa opens the car door.

  C. Grandpa tells Brian a story.

  D. Grandpa flies a kite with his dad.

7. This passage is an example of which kind of writing?

  A. poetry

  B. fairy tale

  C. fiction story

  D. drama

Reading Strategies

Writers can be tricky. They don't always tell you everything in what they write. (They do that to make their stories more interesting and exciting.) Usually it is up to you to figure things out for yourself. In this lesson, you'll learn strategies (or tips) to do just that. You'll learn how to make connections between what you already know and what you are reading. You will also learn how to figure out what the author has hidden "in between the lines." As you'll see, that's part of the fun of reading.

Tip 1 **Link your reading to yourself.**

Later in this lesson, you'll read a passage about the game *Rock, Scissors, Paper*. But before you do, think about what you already know about the topic. Do you know a version of this game already? Have you seen others playing it? Keep asking yourself these kinds of questions before you read a passage.

Also, ask yourself what you wish to learn about a topic. A helpful way to do this is by using a K-W-L chart. "K" stands for what you *know*, "W" stands for what you *want to know*, and "L" stands for what you've *learned* about the topic after reading the passage.

1. What do you know about the game *Rock, Scissors, Paper*? Write anything that comes to mind in the "K" part of the chart. In the "W" part of the chart, write down some questions you might have about the topic. For now, leave the "L" part of the chart empty. You'll come back to that later.

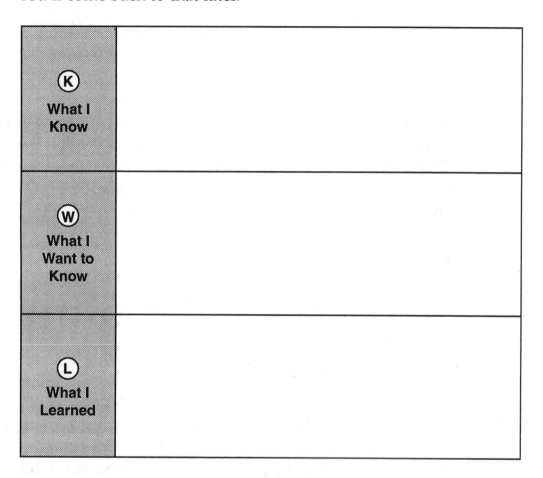

Tip 2 Ask questions as you read.

As you begin reading, ask yourself questions such as the following:

- Do I understand what the author is saying?

- Does this make sense to me?

- What is the passage mostly about?

Mark any parts of the passage that seem difficult to understand. You may wish to go back to those parts later.

As you read the passage, you may find that you have more ideas or questions to write in your K-W-L chart. Continue to make connections between the passage and your life, and jot those connections down in your chart.

Directions: Read the following passage. As you read, remember these tips:

- Link your reading to yourself.
- Ask questions as you read.

Ching! Chang! Pok!
by Christine Thomas

Imagine that you are walking down a street in Beijing, China. You come upon a group of boys and girls playing a game. Two of the boys each wave a fist up and down and chant, *"Ching! Chang! Pok!"* Even though you have never heard these words before, you probably know who wins the game. One boy shows two fingers, and the other shows a flat hand. You know the first boy wins because scissors beat paper in rock, paper, scissors.

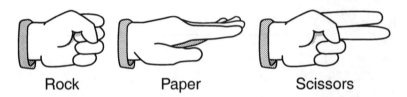

Rock   Paper   Scissors

You have probably seen or played rock, paper, scissors many times, but you might not know that the game began many years ago in Asia, and is now played in almost every country in the world. Since its beginnings, the game has taken many different forms, but certain parts of the game are always the same. In most forms of the game, two or three players raise their fists, bouncing them up and down as they chant the words for each sign of the game. For example, in Japan, the players shout, *"Ishi! Hasami! Kami!"* (stone, scissors, paper). The third time they raise their fists, each player makes a sign for stone (a fist), scissors (two fingers), or paper (a flat hand). In the game, stones break scissors, scissors cut paper, and paper covers stones. The person showing the strongest sign wins.

So the next time you need to make an important decision—like who gets to be first in line, or who gets to have the last piece of pizza—don't just flip a coin. Play a quick game of *Ching! Chang! Pok!* ❖

Tip 3 **When you finish reading, figure out what the passage is mostly about.**

Take a minute to think about the main idea of the passage. Then, if you need to, go back and skim the passage for the most important points that support the main idea.

2. What sentence best describes the main idea of "*Ching! Chang! Pok!*"?

    A. Scissors can cut paper, and paper can cover rocks.

    B. In China, children shout the words *ching, chang,* and *pok.*

    C. The player with the strongest sign gets to have the first turn.

    D. Rock, paper, scissors is a fun game with an interesting history.

3. List at least two ideas that support the main idea of "*Ching! Chang! Pok!*"

_____

_____

"*Ching! Chang! Pok!*" is an example of **nonfiction** (writing that explains real things). But if you are reading a made-up story, retell the most important events in your mind. Ask yourself questions such as *How did the main characters solve their problem?* You will learn more about made-up stories in Unit 3.

Tip 4 **Read between the lines.**

Have you ever heard the saying "read between the lines"? It just means reading "deeper." Authors usually don't tell you every single thing in plain language. Instead, they make their writing more interesting by leaving some things for you to figure out.

4. In English, *ching, chang, pok* means

    A. win, lose, tie.   C. fist, fingers, hand.

    B. *ishi, hasami, kami.*   D. rock, scissors, paper.

See how easy it is to read between the lines? In "*Ching! Chang! Pok!*" the author doesn't just say, "*Ching! Chang! Pok!* is the same thing as rock, paper, scissors." Instead she says that if you saw people playing the game *Ching! Chang! Pok!* in China, you would be able to understand what they're playing by the actions they make with their hands.

Tip 5 **Take time to look at the pictures.**

Whenever the author includes something to look at—such as illustrations and diagrams—it's probably there for a reason. Ask yourself: *Does the diagram tell me something important? Does this picture say something not included in the passage?* Think about why the author chose to include them.

5. How do the illustrations of the hands help you to understand *Rock, Scissors, Paper* better?

   _____

   _____

Tip 6 **Jot down what you learned in your K-W-L chart.**

This is the best part of making a K-W-L chart. Now that you've learned some new information about the game *Rock, Scissors, Paper*, go back and fill in the "L" part of your chart. Try to list as many new facts as you can, based on the passage.

Reading Strategies
Lesson 8 Review

When reading any passage, remember the following tips:

- Link your reading to yourself.

- Ask questions as you read.

- When you finish reading, figure out what the passage is mostly about.

- Read between the lines.

- Take time to look at the pictures.

- Jot down what you learned in your K-W-L chart.

Practice Passage

Directions: Read the passage and answer the questions that follow.

The Biggest Animal That Ever Lived
by Ted Remington

What are the biggest animals that ever lived? Are they elephants? Elephants are pretty big compared to people, but they're not the biggest animals ever. Could they be giant dinosaurs like tyrannosaurus rex (tuh-RAN-uh-SORE-us-REX) or brontosaurus (BRON-tuh-SORE-us)? When those animals lived millions of years ago, they were bigger than elephants are today. But dinosaurs weren't the biggest animals, either.

Here are some hints: The biggest animals do not live on land as elephants do. They are not extinct as dinosaurs are. These animals live in the sea, and some of them are living today. Have you guessed the answer yet? Blue whales are the biggest animals that have ever lived on Earth.

All whales are big compared to people, but blue whales are huge. A full-grown blue whale can be as long as three school buses parked end to end. And it can weigh as much as 30 elephants put together! Just the heart of a blue whale is as big as a small car. A blue whale can hold enough air in its lungs to stay underwater for almost an hour without taking a breath.

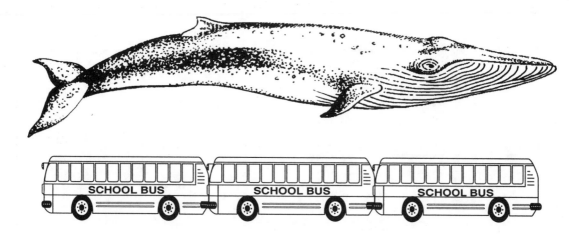

You might think that such a huge animal would be scary and fierce like tyrannosaurus rex. But blue whales are really very gentle. Have you ever heard someone say they are afraid of being swallowed by a whale? They shouldn't be. Although a blue whale's body is huge, it can't swallow anything as big as a person. In fact, blue whales eat very tiny shrimp-like animals called *krill*. Most krill are only an inch or two long.

How can such huge animals stay alive if they eat only tiny sea animals? The answer is, they eat a lot! An adult blue whale eats two tons of krill every day. That's about the same as eating a very large car.

You might not think whales are much like people. After all, blue whales are huge, and you are not. Blue whales live in the sea, and you live on land. But like people, whales are mammals. Whales have hair on their bodies, though not a lot of hair, as you do. Their babies are born alive as you were born, not hatched from eggs. Mother whales feed their babies milk from their bodies, just as human mothers can give milk to their babies. And all whales breathe air, just as you breathe air.

Because blue whales are so big, they have no real enemies except people. Many years ago, whales were hunted and killed for the oil their bodies contain. Until recently, whales also were hunted for food. By now, so many blue whales have been killed that scientists are worried. They are afraid all blue whales will soon be gone from our planet. If that happens, no one will ever get another chance to see the biggest animal that ever lived. That would be very sad for all of us. ❖

Sample Reading Strategies Questions

1. Which sentence tells what the passage is mostly about?
   A. Whales are mammals, just like people.
   B. Whales can stay under water for a long time.
   C. Whales are the biggest animals that have ever lived.
   D. Whales are bigger than elephants and even dinosaurs.

2. In the first paragraph, why does the writer make the reader guess what the largest animal ever is?
   A. to make the passage longer
   B. to show he is smarter than the reader
   C. to make the passage more interesting
   D. to show what he knows about elephants

Additional Practice Questions

3. A full-grown blue whale is about as heavy as what?
   A. 1 dinosaur
   B. 30 elephants
   C. 2 tons of krill
   D. 3 school buses

4. Why would someone read this passage?
   A. to learn about blue whales
   B. to find out about shrimp-like krill
   C. to enjoy a funny story about whales
   D. to understand facts about mammals

5. Blue whales are dying out mostly because they
   A. get too little food.
   B. are hunted by people.
   C. grow too big for their homes.
   D. are eaten by other sea animals.

6. Which word has the same vowel sound as *weigh*?
   A. wet
   B. white
   C. wed
   D. way

Lesson 9

A Treasure Map to Knowledge

Start at the oak tree behind the playground. Take 7 steps north. Now turn east and take 5 steps. Face south and take 8 steps backwards. Dig three feet down to find the treasure.

Sometimes when you are looking for information in a book, you may wish someone would hand you a treasure map leading you straight to what you need. Luckily, most books come with tools that work a lot like maps. If you learn how to use these tools, you will have no trouble finding what you're looking for.

Tip 1 Judge a book by its cover.

No, we don't mean you can tell whether a book is good just by looking at it. But you can tell a lot from the information that's on the cover, such as the **title** (the name of the book). You can also tell a lot from the titles of magazine articles, websites, and so on.

Imagine you've been assigned to write a report about owls for your science teacher. After searching the library, you've found three books with the word *owl* in the title:

> *The Night Owl's Guide to Coffee*
>
> *North American Owls*
>
> *Hootie the Owl and Other Stories*

Before you start paging through every one of these books looking for information about owls, you can probably decide to leave a few of them on the shelf.

1. Which book most likely contains scientific facts about owls?

_____

Tip 2 **Use the tools inside the book.**

Now that you've found a book that matches the topic of your report (owls), it's time to find the information you need. You could read the whole book until you find what you want. Or, you could use the tools that the author put in to help you find what you need. The first tool is called the table of contents.

Table of contents

The **table of contents** is an outline of a book. It is always found in the first few pages, and it tells you the main topics in the book.

Chapter headings are like book titles because they tell what sort of information you'll find in each chapter. You can skip right to the information you want by paying attention to the chapter titles. Chapter headings often appear at the top of each page, so you can find the chapters more easily. (Also, within each chapter you may find titles that divide the writing into smaller chunks. Pay attention to those as you read, too.)

2. Which page would you turn to if you wanted to know what kind of food owls eat?

    A. 21

    B. 32

    C. 41

    D. 71

3. Which page would you turn to if you wanted to know where to find owls?

    A. 21

    B. 32

    C. 41

    D. 71

4. What chapter describes different kinds of owls?

    A. 1

    B. 2

    C. 3

    D. 4

5. What is Chapter 6 about?

_____

The index

Another tool many books include is the **index**. A book's index lists every topic in the book. The list is in alphabetical order (first, the topics beginning with A, then, the topics beginning with B, and so on). It contains many more details than the table of contents. An index also gives you the page number on which you can find each topic. The index is found in the back of a book.

Here is part of the index from *North American Owls.* Use it to answer the questions that follow.

Index

barn owls, 13
beaks, 17
colors, protective, 20, 27, 36
eating habits, 32–40
eyesight, 23
facial disks, 19, 32
feathers, 2, 15, 36
flight, 3, 7, 14–20, 32–33
grass owls, 12, 15, 18, 35
habitats, 3, 8–11, 21–31
hearing, 22, 24
hunting, 14–21
nesting, 12, 13, 14, 25, 27

6. On which pages could you read about how owls hunt?
   A. 22 and 24
   B. 12, 13, and 14
   C. 14 through 21
   D. 8, 9, 10, and 11

7. On which pages could you read about the eating habits of owls?
   A. 19 and 32
   B. 3, 4, and 7
   C. 32 through 40
   D. 32 through 84

Glossary

Some books have a **glossary**, which is like a dictionary of every important word in the book. The glossary lists words in alphabetical order. It is found in the back of a book. Here is part of the glossary from *North American Owls.*

Glossary

barn owl	one of two families of owls; there are 10 kinds of barn owl
bird of prey	a bird that kills and eats other animals
beak	the bill of a bird
habitat	a place where a plant or animal naturally lives and grows
plumage	the feathers of a bird

A Treasure Map to Knowledge
Lesson 9 Review

When you are looking for information in a book, use these tips to find exactly what you're looking for:

- Judge a book by its cover. (The title tells what a book is about.)

- Use the tools inside the book. (The table of contents, chapter headings, index, and glossary can tell you where to look.)

Sample Book Tools Questions

Directions: Mrs. Kamp's class has been assigned to write a report about a real job or career. Adam has chosen to write about cowboys and cowgirls. He has gone to the library and found several books. Help Adam find the information he needs by answering the following questions.

1. Which of the following books should Adam NOT read to learn about real cowboys and cowgirls?
   A. *Life on the Range*
   B. *The Cowboy from Mars*
   C. *The History of the Cowgirl*
   D. *Modern Cowboys and Cowgirls*

2. Which of these books will most likely help Adam write his report?
   A. *Famous Film Cowgirls*
   B. *Tales of the Lone Ranger*
   C. *A Day in the Life of a Cowboy*
   D. *Cowhide on Canvas: Cowboy Paintings*

3. Which of the following websites will most likely help Adam research for his report?
   A. *Beth's World of Horses*
   B. *Cowboy Boots and Silver Spurs*
   C. *Cherry Hill Rodeo Photography*
   D. *Cowboy and Cowgirl Careers and Information*

4. While reading a book about the skills necessary to be a cowboy or cowgirl, Adam comes across the word *lasso*. If he didn't know the meaning of the word, where could Adam look?
   A. the index
   B. the glossary
   C. the front cover
   D. the chapter headings

After focusing his topic, Adam has decided to write mostly about how cowboys' jobs have changed in the last few years. He is looking at the table of contents from *America's Cowboys*.

Table of Contents

Chapter	Page
1 The First Cowboys	3
2 Tools of the Trade	22
3 Rounding Up the Herd	41
4 Thousand-Mile Cattle Drive	60
5 Cowboys in the 21st Century	79

---

5. On what page will Adam find information about recent changes in the job of being a cowboy?

    A. 41

    B. 60

    C. 79

    D. 98

6. Which chapter probably talks about saddles and lassos?

    A. Tools of the Trade

    B. The First Cowboys

    C. Rounding Up the Herd

    D. Thousand-Mile Cattle Drive

7. If Adam couldn't decide which chapter talked about saddles and lassos, what should he do to find out?

    A. read the book's title

    B. read the whole book

    C. use the book's glossary

    D. use the book's index

Lesson 10

Dealing with Directions

Sometimes you read for fun. Sometimes you read to learn. And sometimes you read to find out how to do something. All kinds of reading are important, but the last kind—the "how-to-do-it" kind—is often the most helpful in everyday life. This lesson will help you learn to follow directions by using what you read.

Some assembly required

Imagine that you have just been given a new toy called Pull Yourself Together! This toy is like a robot, except that you get to put it together. But how do you get from this—

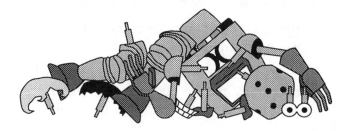

—to this?

Tip 1 **First, read through the directions from beginning to end.**

When you use directions, read them all the way through one time. This way you will have a general idea of everything you need to do. Then ask yourself the following question:

✔ Do I understand each step?

Imagine your Pull Yourself Together! has come with this set of instructions.

INSTRUCTIONS
Read Carefully

1. Choose a hair piece. Press the hair piece onto the top of the head.

2. Add the eye piece to the eye holes. Add the nose and mouth.

3. Add an ear to each side of the head.

4. Press the head onto the body. It should click when it is firmly in place.

5. Press the left arm into the left shoulder of the body. Now add the right arm to the right shoulder. These should click when they are in place.

6. Press the left leg onto the body, then the right.

If you don't understand one of the steps, go back and reread it.

1. To put your robot together, you will have to do all of the following except
   A. add the nose and mouth.
   B. press the fingers onto the hands.
   C. add the right arm to the right shoulder.
   D. press the hair piece onto the top of the head.

Tip 2 **Gather all the materials needed.**

After reading through the directions, gather all the tools and materials needed to follow those directions. Then you will not have to stop to find things like hammers, screwdrivers, string, bowls, forks, flour, sugar, and so on.

   2. Which of the following parts do the directions call for?
      A. elbow pieces
      B. hand pieces
      C. foot pieces
      D. hair pieces

Tip 3 **Follow the directions in order without skipping any steps.**

After you gather your materials, it's time to begin. Where do you begin? At the beginning, of course.

Complete the steps one at a time. And be sure to complete them in order. If you complete directions out of order, sometimes things will not turn out the way they should. You may wish to check off each step as it is completed.

   3. Which of these steps comes first in the directions?
      A. Press the head onto the body.
      B. Add the eye piece to the eye holes.
      C. Press the left leg onto the body, then the right.
      D. Press the left arm into the left shoulder of the body.

   4. If you skipped step #5, your robot would be missing its
      A. arms.
      B. hair.
      C. nose.
      D. mouth.

Tip 4 Use direction pictures to help you understand the written steps.

Many directions give pictures showing how to complete the steps. Look at these carefully as you follow the steps. But don't use only the pictures. The words are just as important. They may tell you things that the pictures do not.

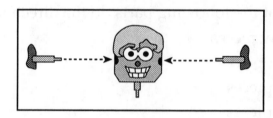

5. Which step does the above picture demonstrate?

   A. step 1

   B. step 2

   C. step 3

   D. step 4

6. What does the picture show that the directions do not mention?

   _____

   _____

Dealing with Directions
Lesson 10 Review

- First, read through the directions from beginning to end.

- Gather all the materials needed.

- Follow the directions in order without skipping any steps.

- Use direction pictures to help you understand the written steps.

Practice Following Directions

Directions: Read the directions and answer the questions that follow.

Popcorn Balls

What you need to make 10 popcorn balls: 2 quarts of popped popcorn   1 large pan
4 1/2 cups of mini marshmallows   1 saucepan
1/4 cup butter   1 large spoon

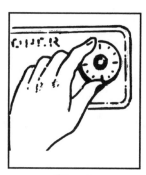

Step 1
Preheat oven
to 350˚F.

Step 2
Pop popcorn.

Step 3
Put popcorn in large
pan and place in
oven to keep warm.

Step 4
Melt butter in
saucepan over very
low heat.

Step 5
As butter melts, pour
in marshmallows and
stir until melted.

Step 6
Using oven mitts,
remove popcorn
from oven.

Step 7
Pour mixture over popcorn.
Stir with spoon until
popcorn is coated.

Step 8
Rub butter on your hands.
Shape popcorn into balls
about the size of tennis balls.

Step 9
Let cool.

Sample Directions Questions

1. How many quarts of popcorn would you need if you wanted to make 20 popcorn balls?

   A. 1   C. 4

   B. 2   D. 5

2. What should you do first when making popcorn balls?

   A. Put butter on your hands.

   B. Read through all the directions.

   C. Put a pan of popcorn in a warm oven.

   D. Melt the marshmallows and butter together.

3. Which of the following is not used in the recipe?

   A. marshmallows

   B. peanut butter

   C. butter

   D. salt

4. You can find out how to form the popcorn balls in which step?

   A. 6   C. 8

   B. 7   D. 9

5. What did the writer forget to add to the "What you need . . . " section?

   A. oven mitts

   B. a large pan

   C. a saucepan

   D. a large spoon

6. After you pour the mixture over the popcorn, you should stir until

   A. the oven is warm.

   B. the butter is melted.

   C. the popcorn is coated.

   D. the marshmallows are added.

All Kinds of Reading

How many kinds of bicycles are there? Dirt bikes, road bikes, a little-bit-of-both bikes, bikes built for one, bikes built for two . . . The list goes on and on. Almost all bicycles have certain things in common, though: wheels, handle bars, brakes, and at least one seat.

Just like bicycles, there are also many different kinds of writing. In this unit, you will learn about a few of them, such as made-up stories, real-life stories, poems, and plays. You will also learn about the kinds of things that many stories have in common, including characters, settings, and plots. You will learn about some of the choices writers make, such as what kinds of words to use. And you will learn how to figure out the message that the writer is trying to get across in a real-life or made-up story.

In This Unit
- *Tell Me a Made-Up Story*
- *All Kinds of Writing*
- *Favorite Stories*
- *Seeing the Writer in the Writing*

Lesson 11

Tell Me a Made-Up Story

A Ghost Story?

The pine trees, dark against the rising moon, whispered softly. The girls sat huddled in warm blankets, waiting for Rachel, their counselor, to begin a ghost story. Puffs of wind played with the campfire, swirling sparks up into the night sky. The flames danced. The girls grew very quiet—and Rachel began in a low voice.

"Once upon a time, there were some people who lived somewhere. A ghost scared them."

Rachel had finished her story. Standing up, she brushed the sand from her pants. "Okay, girls," she said. "Time for bed."

"Come on!" Karen said. "That was no story! We don't know anything about the people. Tell us about the *characters*."

"Yeah," her friend Heather said. "And we don't know where it happened or when it happened. Tell us about the *setting*."

"We don't even know what happened," Marsha said, sounding disappointed. "Tell us about the *plot*." ❖

Tip 1 A story has characters, a setting, and a plot.

Fiction always has **characters**. Usually, the characters are people, but they can be animals (such as *Bambi* or *The Three Little Pigs*), monsters (such as vampires), and strange creatures (such as Dr. Seuss's Grinch or Aladdin's genie). They can even be trees, cars, or trains that talk. (Do you remember *The Little Engine that Could*?)

Stories also give the reader a **setting**, which is a place and time for the story to happen. The setting might be on a sailing ship, in the mountains, at a ballpark—or even on the moon. The story might take place today, 2,000 years in the past, or sometime far into the future.

Things have to happen in a story, too. These happenings are called the story's **plot**.

Read the following sentences. Then circle the word that tells whether the sentence is mostly about characters, setting, or plot.

1. Ten-year-old Randy has a cousin, Louise.

    characters   setting   plot

2. A bicycle crashes, throwing its rider into the air.

    characters   setting   plot

3. The floor of the cave is cold, and its walls are wet.

    characters   setting   plot

4. The lake looks like a mirror in the moonlight.

    characters   setting   plot

5. Describe the setting, characters, or plot of one of your favorite stories.

    _____

    _____

    _____

Tip 2 Get to know the characters by watching their actions and by listening to what they say.

You can get to know the characters in a story if you pay attention to details. You can learn what the characters look like, how they think, and how they act.

Read this passage from a mystery story. Pay close attention to the details. Then answer the questions that follow.

Jody and her sister Beth ran down the bike path beside Jackson Highway. Jody was frightened. Her long black hair streamed in the wind. A bright red book bag flopped wildly on her back. Her unbuttoned raincoat flapped in the wind like the wings of a giant yellow bird.

Beth ran beside her with the grace of a deer. She was breathing easily and seemed unaware of any danger. Her biggest concern was trying to keep up with her older sister, who seemed to be running out of control.

When they got to Oak Street, they cut through Mr. Henderson's lawn. Every now and then, Jody looked over her shoulder to see if Mrs. Parker was still following her.

The girls didn't stop running until they reached Elm Street and the safety of their own front steps. Beth ran inside, heading for the kitchen. Gasping for breath, Jody sat down, flipped the book bag onto her knees, and searched for a pencil. Settling for a stubby green crayon, she ripped a page from her third-grade spelling book. With trembling hands, she scribbled a quick note. ❖

Michelle,

    I can't meet you here after school today. I have to do something very important. See you tomorrow—I hope!

                    Jody C.

6. Which of the following best describes Jody and Beth?
   A. Jody is frightened; Beth is unaware of danger.
   B. Jody lives on Oak Street; Beth lives on Elm Street.
   C. Jody writes with a crayon; Beth writes with a pencil.
   D. Jody is running home; Beth is walking home slowly.

7. Where does Mr. Henderson live?
   A. on Elm Street
   B. on Oak Street
   C. near a bike path
   D. along Jackson Highway

8. Which word best tells how Jody feels?
   A. angry
   B. fearful
   C. cheerful
   D. grouchy

9. Which character does the author want readers to fear?
   A. Jody
   B. Michelle
   C. Mrs. Parker
   D. Mr. Henderson

10. In your own words, tell how Jody is dressed and what she looks like.

   _____

   _____

   _____

   _____

Tip 3 **Use details to picture the setting.**

Stories also have a setting. The setting is the time and place in which the action happens. Longer stories and books may have many different settings. Again, look for details. They will tell you when and where the story takes place.

Read this historical-fiction passage and answer the questions that follow.

> It was New Year's Eve, 1815. Captain Henry stood at the wheel of his sleek, new steamboat, the *Washington*. From the wheelhouse atop his boat, he peered down the moonlit Mississippi River. He watched carefully for shallow waters, sandbars, and tree snags. Bright sparks and heavy black smoke poured out of the boat's tall smokestacks. The soot-filled clouds trailed upriver and floated on the still night air. Steam hissed from the boilers. And, softly, the tinkle of a piano drifted up from the carpeted main cabin.
>
> *She's making good time*, the captain thought. *We should be in New Orleans before midnight.*

11. Which words best describe the night?
    A. clear and windy   C. moonlit and still
    B. cloudy and windy   D. clear and bright

12. Which words best describe the setting of this passage?
    A. in New Orleans, Louisiana
    B. near some sandbars and tree snags
    C. aboard a Mississippi River steamboat
    D. near the piano in a carpeted main cabin

13. What time of year does the action take place?
    A. summer   C. winter
    B. autumn   D. spring

Tip 4 **Find the problems to learn about the plot.**

Stories wouldn't be very interesting without plots. Most of the time, the plot is about some kind of problems the characters face. These problems make the story exciting.

Most stories have a *main* problem and other, smaller problems. The main character may have a problem with another character, such as a parent, a neighbor, or a teacher. Or, the problem might be with a thing, such as a storm, a wild animal, or a broken bicycle. Sometimes the problem will be within the character. *Should I do this, or should I do that?* the character will wonder.

14. In the passage about Jody and Beth, what is the main problem?
    A. Beth is unaware of any danger.
    B. Beth is trying to keep up with Jody.
    C. Jody is being followed by Mrs. Parker.
    D. Jody can't meet Michelle after school.

———— Tell Me a Made-Up Story ————
Lesson 11 Review

When answering questions about stories, remember the following tips:

- A story has characters, a setting, and a plot.
- Get to know the characters by watching their actions and by listening to what they say.
- Use details to picture the setting.
- Find the problems to learn about the plot.

Practice Passage

Directions: Read the passage and answer the questions that follow.

from

The Secret of the Old Barn
by Robyn Winchell

Tio[1] Roberto said it would be the perfect way to spend a rainy afternoon. Angie and Rosa agreed. Their aunt and uncle's old barn hadn't been used for years, but the roof was good, and it didn't leak. Although it might be a little dusty, playing in the hayloft would be more fun than staying in the farmhouse for yet another rainy day.

The girls climbed a ladder toward an opening in the hayloft floor above them. They could hear rain beating on the roof and the sound of thunder in the distance. Pigeons cooed softly from the rafters high above them.

"This will be fun," Angie said as her head rose above the loft floor. She scrambled to her feet in the dusty hay. Rosa followed her sister into the loft like a shadow.

"We can pretend we're mountain climbers," Rosa said, looking at the mounds of hay.

Just then, both girls froze. Something dark and furry hurried across the floor in front of them and disappeared into the hay.

"What was that?" Angie asked.

"Why, it looked like Beanie, Tia[2] Carmen's cat," Rosa said. "Tia Carmen says she hasn't seen Beanie for more than two weeks."

"There she is again," Angie said, pointing to the cat, which was now lying on top of the straw, <u>flicking</u> its black tail from side to side.

---

[1] **Tio** is the Spanish word for *uncle*.
[2] **Tia** is the Spanish word for *aunt*.

The girls struggled over piles of loose hay, then bent down to pet the cat. It began to purr loudly. After a few minutes, Beanie stood, stretched, and disappeared into the hay once again. The girls began to hear soft noises coming from under the hay.

"What's making those sounds?" Angie asked.

"I don't know," Rosa replied.

The girls waited quietly, listening to the soft sounds coming from the hay. In a very short time, Beanie came back out. This time she was carrying a small spotted kitten in her mouth.

"Beanie's had kittens!" Angie said. "And look!" She pointed to a small tunnel in the hay. Four more blue-eyed kittens wobbled toward the girls.

"Oh, they're so cute!" Rosa said. She carefully picked up the littlest one. It squirmed in her hand and mewed a tiny cry.

Beanie gave a warning meow and batted at Rosa's hand with one paw.

"I think you'd better put it down," Angie said. "It doesn't look like Beanie thinks they're ready for company yet. Let's come back later and bring her a saucer of milk."

"Good idea," Rosa said, placing the baby kitten next to its mother. "See you later, Beanie's babies!" she said. ❖

Sample Fiction Elements Questions

1. What time of day do the events in this passage take place?
   A. morning   C. afternoon
   B. noon   D. evening

2. Which of the following best describes the setting for most of this passage?
   A. a treehouse   C. a barn
   B. a cabin   D. a mountain

3. How are Angie and Rosa most alike?
   A. They are both in the third grade.
   B. They are both afraid to climb ladders.
   C. They are both afraid of old buildings.
   D. They are sisters who enjoy each other's company.

Additional Practice Questions

4. Why do the girls play in the barn?
   A. They want to practice mountain climbing.
   B. Tia Carmen wants them to find her cat.
   C. They want to listen to the sound of pigeons cooing.
   D. It is raining, and they don't want to stay in the house.

5. How many of Beanie's kittens did Angie and Rosa see?
   A. three
   B. four
   C. five
   D. six

6. In paragraph 8, what does the word *flicking* mean?
   A. hiding
   B. flopping
   C. holding
   D. chewing

7. Which of the following best describes the passage?
   A. poem
   B. folktale
   C. fantasy
   D. fiction

8. What will probably happen next in the story?
   A. Tia Carmen will tell the girls to clean the barn.
   B. The girls will decide to play outside in the rain.
   C. The girls will tell their aunt and uncle about the kittens.
   D. Tio Roberto will say that the hayloft is not a safe place to play.

All Kinds of Writing

"What do you have there?" Dad asked.

"A book," Sam said.

"What kind of book?"

Sam wondered why Dad was asking so many questions. "I don't know," she said. "It's just a book."

Dad laughed. "Well, what kind of book is it? Is it real or made-up? Is it a play? Is it a dictionary? A cookbook? A joke book? A . . . ?"

There are so many different things to read! Newspapers, magazines, books, comic books, websites, CD-ROMs . . . It can be hard to keep them all straight in your mind. But did you know that most writing is one of these four types?

- fiction
- nonfiction
- drama
- poetry

Each of these types of writing has something special that makes it different from the others. As you read the tips in this lesson, you'll learn how to tell what kind of writing you're reading. The next time someone asks you what you're reading, you can be sure of your answer.

Tip 1 **Fiction tells about events that have been imagined.**

In Lesson 11, you learned about fictional story parts: characters, setting, and plot. But how do you tell the difference between a fictional story and a real-life (nonfictional) story?

Some stories are true, and others are made up. Any made-up story is fiction. No matter what the story is about, if it is imagined, it's fiction. Most of the time, you will be able to easily tell that a story is fiction. A story about a kid who has a time machine, or about a bunch of talking pigs, is probably fiction.

What about stories that are about a normal person doing normal things? How can you tell whether they are fiction?

If the story tells you what each character is thinking, the story is probably fiction. Unless people say what's on their minds, it would be impossible for the author to know what they are thinking. To do that, the author would have to make the story up.

Fictional stories often give a lot of extra details. If a story tells you that George Washington ate a bowl of oatmeal with raisins, and that it smelled very good, then the story is fiction. Nobody knows how George Washington's oatmeal smelled, so the author must have made that up.

1. Read these sentences and answer the question that follows.

   Sally could feel the heat of the dragon's flaming breath from her hiding place. She thought she'd soon be toast.

   Are these sentences an example of fiction? How can you tell?

   _____

   _____

2. Which of the following is most likely from a fictional story?
   A. Young Jesse Jackson was a football player and baseball star.
   B. Put the dough on a flat surface and press it down with your fingers.
   C. Jessica felt the warm glow of the purple moon against her scaly arms.
   D. The coastline of this tropical East African country is over 1,700 miles long.

3. Which of the following book titles is most likely the title to a fictional story?
   A. *How to Build a Birdhouse*   C. *My Dog, Speck*
   B. *The Nine Planets*   D. *Unicorns of Misty Mountain*

Tip 2 **Nonfiction tells about real events and explains real things.**

Writing that is not made up is called **nonfiction**. Nonfiction includes true stories and history, plus science writing, news stories, opinions, and instructions. If you were to read a book called *How to Grow Great Tomatoes*, it probably would not tell you a true story, but it would list a lot of facts about tomatoes and give you a set of instructions to follow.

Facts are a major part of what makes nonfiction different from fiction. Every event shown in a nonfiction story can be checked to make sure it really happened. A book that explains how something works or that describes places or things also can be checked to make sure its information is true.

4. Which of the following sentences is probably an example of nonfiction writing?
   A. Rover barked at the passing cars and wondered why he was not allowed to drive.
   B. The fairy's wings fluttered as she gently came to rest in the boy's hand.
   C. After his baseball career ended, Michael Jordan returned to basketball.
   D. "You'll never catch me!" shouted Alex, who then snapped his fingers and disappeared.

5. Explain how you chose your answer to Number 4.

   _____

   _____

6. Which of the following book titles is most likely the title of a nonfiction story?
   A. *Mrs. Piggle-Wiggle's Farm*
   B. *The Mouse and the Motorcycle*
   C. *Shirley Temple Black: The Story of My Life*
   D. *The Adventures of the Black Hand Gang*

Tip 3 A drama is a story that is written for actors to perform.

A story that is acted out is called a **drama**. The story may be acted out as a play on a stage, as a movie, as a TV show, as a radio program, or even by students in a class. Whatever the story is about, drama is written in a special way that tells the actors what to say, where to move, and sometimes even what costumes to wear.

There are two main ways that drama stories tell the actors what to do. The first is called **stage directions**. These are directions that tell the actors where to stand, where the story is set, and so on. They are not read to the audience. A stage direction might look like this:

(BILL enters carrying a chicken and a calculator.)

This direction tells the actor playing Bill to come into the scene holding a chicken and a calculator. So far, he does not have anything to say. An author tells the actors what to say using dialogue. **Dialogue** (DYE-uh-log) is what the characters say.

BILL: Well, maybe my chicken can't write his name—but he knows how to use a calculator!

Dramas tell stories through the things the actors say and do. There is not much detail to the setting. The author may write that the setting is the inside of a classroom in California in the year 2001 but will probably not tell more than that.

Practice Activity: Types of Writing

Read the following passages and determine what type of writing each one is.

Passage 1

Captain Alonso looked behind her. The space slugs were still on their way. Ahead of her loomed the giant Martian lizard, its mouth open, its tongue stretching out towards her. "I've got to time this just right!" she said, ducking. The space slugs jumped toward her and went right into the lizard's mouth.

Passage 2

LUCY: (bored) I really love this homework.
GAYLE: Then why don't you marry it?
(LUCY gets up and walks away.)
GAYLE: Hey! I was just kidding!

Passage 3

Lightning is a giant spark of electricity. During storms, electricity builds up in the rain clouds. Once in a while, it jumps from one place to another, just as it jumps from your finger to a doorknob when you get a shock.

7. What type of writing is Passage 1?

_____

8. Which passage is nonfiction?

_____

9. Name one character from the drama passage.

_____

Tip 4 **Poems paint pictures in our minds.**

In some ways, poems are like most other kinds of writing. They can tell a story. They can paint beautiful pictures in our minds. They can be serious or they can be funny. They can be about made-up things, or they can be about real things. And they can make us feel happy or sad.

But poems usually don't look like other kinds of writing. Instead of letting the words run all the way across the page, a poet will decide where each line should end. A poet may use words that rhyme to end each line (but not always). And some poems may be very short or split into small chunks called **stanzas**.

Look at the following poem to see how each stanza is made up of four
short lines. (Stanzas, like paragraphs, can be any length.)

Marvin Made a Model Ship
by Michael Acton

Marvin made a model ship
Of playing cards and glue.
It was a graceful sailing ship
When Marvin was all through.

But, getting up one early morn,
He found his ship a wreck.
His brother Johnny smashed it flat
When Dad called, Hit the deck!

Poets are very careful to choose words that show exactly how they feel
and that help the reader have those feelings, too. There are many
unusual ways a poet can use words. Two of the poetic writing tools are
listed here.

Tip 5 *Boom! Whoosh!* That's onomatopoeia!

You may be wondering just what that long word is. **Onomatopoeia**
(ON-uh-MOTT-uh-PEE-uh) is just a big word that means "words that
sound like what they mean." For example, if you were going to write a
poem about fireworks, you would probably use words like *WHACK*
and *POP* to describe the loud sounds. Each of those words sounds like
what it describes.

If you were simply to say the fireworks exploded, then you would not
be using onomatopoeia, because the word *explode* doesn't actually
sound like an explosion.

10. Think of at least three more onomatopoeic (sound) words. One has
    been filled in for you.

    splash _____

    _____

    _____

Tip 6 **Like letters often create like sounds.**

When a poet puts several words near each other that begin with the same consonant sound, the poet is using **alliteration** (uh-LIT-er-AY-shun). You have probably heard someone say "Peter Piper picked a peck of pickled peppers." It's a silly-sounding thing to say, but it's a very good example of alliteration. Almost every word in the sentence begins with the letter *p*.

A poet might use alliteration to get our attention, to make us laugh, or to give us a better idea of how something sounds. For example, in this sentence—

The big blue ball bounced and bounded back to the basement.

—we can almost hear the sound of the ball thumping its way down the stairs.

11. In the last example, what letter was repeated using alliteration?
    A. *a*   C. *c*
    B. *b*   D. *d*

12. Now try writing your own sentence using alliteration.

_____

_____

All Kinds of Writing
Lesson 12 Review

- Fiction tells about events that have been imagined.
- Nonfiction tells about real events and explains real things.
- A drama is a story that is written for actors to perform.
- Poems paint pictures in our minds.
- *Boom! Whoosh!* That's onomatopoeia!
- Like letters often create like sounds.

Practice Passage

Directions: Read this passage, then answer the questions that follow.

Toy Talk
by Mickey Toom

At twilight, toys tucked in their box
Lay still, except for moonlight talks.
One winter night the red drum said,
"The world's so loud it hurts my head."

"No, no," the windup monkey's voice
<u>Insisted</u> as he told the toys,
"Let's talk about the world I've found.
It back flips every time I'm wound!"

The top was silent till she said,
"The world roars round and round my head.
Sometimes it gets in such a tizzy
My face turns green and I get dizzy."

"No. None of you is right," the ball
Said loudly to them one and all.
"The world goes up when I go down,
Boing! Boing! Just like a circus clown."

The hobby horse across the room
Creaked gently in the dust and gloom.
He'd watched the edges of the earth
And *knew* the world rocked back and forth.

All Kinds of Writing Sample Questions

1. What kind of writing is "Toy Talk"?
    A. poetry
    B. drama
    C. fiction
    D. nonfiction

2. How can you tell what kind of writing "Toy Talk" is?
    A. It uses stage directions.
    B. It tells about real events.
    C. It is made up of lines and stanzas.
    D. It contains many made-up details.

3. Which of the following lines contains an example of onomatopoeia?
    A. The world goes up when I go down,
    B. Boing! Boing! Just like a circus clown.
    C. He'd watched the edges of the earth
    D. And *knew* the world rocked back and forth.

4. Read the following line from the poem.

    The world roars round and round my head.

    This line is a good example of
    A. real events.
    B. using dialogue.
    C. using stage directions.
    D. using alliteration.

Additional Practice Questions

5. "Toy Talk" is the _____ of the passage.
   A. title
   B. index
   C. glossary
   D. chapter heading

6. When does "Toy Talk" take place?
   A. in the afternoon
   B. on a winter night
   C. just before summer
   D. late in the morning

7. What is the main idea of "Toy Talk"?
   A. At night, the toys talk in their box.
   B. Each toy sees the world differently.
   C. One winter night, the drum said his head hurt.
   D. The hobby horse knew the world rocked back and forth.

8. What does the word *insisted* mean?
   A. whistled
   B. complained
   C. talked loudly
   D. demanded

Lesson 13

Favorite Stories

As you learned in Lesson 11, the events that make up a story are called the plot. In most plots, the characters have a problem, and the story is mostly about how the problem gets solved. (Sometimes it can be about how the problem *doesn't* get solved.) Reading about how the characters solve their problem can sometimes teach you a lesson about life.

Tip 1 **Understanding how the story ends will help you figure out the author's message.**

If you have ever heard or read the story "Goldilocks and the Three Bears," you know that there is a special message in the story. A young girl goes into a bear family's house, sits in their chairs, eats their food, and tries out their beds. Because the bears come home and chase her away, you can tell that the author of the story wants you to learn that you should not use other people's things without asking.

Almost every story has some kind of message. Some stories are made up in order to teach us lessons about life. In this lesson, we will look at some of the kinds of stories that teach lessons, how they came to be, and what they are usually about.

Folktales: The first stories

Hundreds of years ago, there were no movies, no television shows, no video games—and, for most people, no books! When people wanted to teach each other or have fun, they made up stories. They would tell the stories over and over so that everyone could learn them. Children would hear the stories, grow up, and tell the stories to their children.

In time, people decided to put their stories on paper. Those old stories are now called **folktales**.

When people made up folktales many years ago, they often had special reasons for telling them. Some of the stories were funny or scary or exciting, but many told the listeners something about the world. Folktales often teach us lessons, such as how to get along with others, or why things happen the way they do.

There are many different kinds of folktales. In this lesson, you will learn about four types: fairy tales, myths, legends, and fables.

Tip 2 **A fairy tale shows good working against evil.**

In a **fairy tale**, evil characters try to hurt good characters or make the good characters do as they say. A good character will then try to stop the evil ones from getting what they want. For example, in the story "Jack and the Beanstalk," a mean giant tries to keep a young man named Jack from going home. Jack must figure out how to get away.

Often, a fairy tale shows magic. For example, Jack uses magic beans to grow the tall beanstalk. In "Sleeping Beauty," a whole kingdom falls under a spell and sleeps for years.

Many fairy tales begin like this:

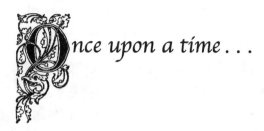

nce upon a time . . .

Most fairy tales end like this:

. . . happily ever after.

When the heroes win and live "happily ever after," the message of the fairy tale is clear: good defeats evil, and love conquers all.

1. What is the name of another fairy tale?

_____

2. Which of the following does NOT usually appear in a fairy tale?
   A. good characters   C. science facts
   B. magic   D. evil characters

Tip 3 **A myth answers a question about the world.**

Like fairy tales, **myths** often tell of good battling evil and include magic. But myths are different because they usually try to answer a question about the world.

Many years ago, people told stories to answer questions like "Why does the sun rise and set?" or "Why does the lake show my reflection?"

Some of the most famous myths come from Greece and Rome, but they are not the only myths. Every place on Earth has myths that tell about the workings of the natural world and how people came to live here.

3. Which of these stories is most likely a myth?
   A. "Bob Goes to Bombay"   C. "Bobo the Mighty"
   B. "Laura Tricks the Troll"   D. "How the Sky Became Blue"

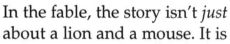

Tip 4 **Fables use simple tales to teach big lessons.**

Many fables show animals acting like people in order to show us how we act.

In the fable "The Lion and the Mouse," a lion catches a mouse to eat for his dinner. The mouse promises to help the lion if the lion will let him go. The lion does not think the mouse could ever help him, but he lets the mouse go. Later on, the lion steps on a thorn and cannot get it out of his paw. The little mouse comes along and takes the thorn out.

In the fable, the story isn't *just* about a lion and a mouse. It is really about how people should help each other, and it tells us that we might be surprised by who is able to help us.

Like "The Lion and the Mouse," most fables are simple stories that are really about big lessons. Some fables don't use animals, but they still make us see that we can often be selfish, foolish, or stubborn.

4. Name another fable that uses animals to teach a lesson.

_____

5. Which of these stories is most likely a fable?
   A. "The Hare and the Tortoise"
   B. "Penelope's Magic Pennies"
   C. "Why There Are Mountains"
   D. "Gus and the Great Glass Gumball"

People think that a man named Aesop was the first to spread many of the fables we know today. Not much is known about Aesop, but he was probably a Greek slave who lived over 2,500 years ago. His stories have been told in many ways and in many cultures, but the messages of those stories remain the same.

The Ant and the Grasshopper
An Aesop fable retold by Rick Zollo

Many, many years ago, a grasshopper spent his summer singing in the tall grass. His neighbor the ant spent the same summer carrying tasty leaves to his home in the ground.

"Why do you work so hard?" asked Grasshopper. "It is too beautiful outside. Summer is the time to play."

The ant kept working. He was not going to let Grasshopper upset his plan of action.

Soon fall came, and after that came winter. Cold winds blew across the sea, chilling the earth. Grasshopper found himself hungry and in need of some food.

"Help me, I'm hungry," Grasshopper said to the ant.

"Didn't I see you during the summer, singing instead of working?" asked Ant.

"Yes, that was me," said shivering Grasshopper.

"You sang all summer," said Ant. "You should dance all winter." ❖

6. What lesson does this fable teach?
    A. You should always share your things with others.
    B. You can't always count on friends when you need them.
    C. You should relax and enjoy the good times while you can.
    D. In good times, you must plan ahead in case hard times come.

Tip 5 Legends show us what it means to be a hero.

Another kind of folktale is called a **legend**. These stories show the lives of brave, strong characters who are based on real people. The heroes of these stories do great things that show us the best parts of ourselves.

In the story of John Henry, a legend of the American West, there is a contest to see who can tunnel through a mountain faster: a steam-powered drilling machine or a great strongman, John Henry. John hammers his way through the mountain and wins the race with his last breath. The story shows us that one of our greatest strengths is the courage to take on challenges and never give up.

Many times, as in the legend of John Henry, we cannot be sure that there was a real person who did all of the things in the story. But usually, at least some part of the legend is true.

7. Which of these characters is from a legend?
   A. Superman
   B. Minnie Mouse
   C. Charlie Brown
   D. Johnny Appleseed

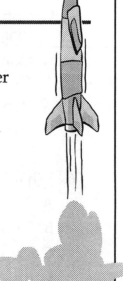

Favorite Stories
Lesson 13 Review

When answering questions about folktales, remember these tips:

- Understanding how the story ends will help you figure out the author's message.

- A fairy tale shows good working against evil.

- A myth answers a question about the world.

- Fables use simple tales to teach big lessons.

- Legends show us what it means to be a hero.

Practice Passage

Directions: Read the passage and answer the questions that follow.

How the Sun Was Saved
Adapted from a Siberian folktale

Once upon a time, evil spirits stole the sun from the animals of the north land. The birds and the beasts had to find their food in the dark. At last they called a meeting. All the animals were there.

An old raven spoke. "We cannot live without the sun. I say we send the polar bear to get it. He is big and strong."

The other animals called out, "Yes, the bear is big and strong."

An old owl did not agree. "Yes, he is strong, but as soon as he finds food, he will forget about the sun."

"Then let us send the wolf," said the raven. "After the bear, he is the strongest, plus he is quicker."

Again the old owl did not agree. "He is quick, but he is greedy. As soon as he finds his first deer, he will forget the sun."

"You are right," said the animals, "but who should we send?"

A tiny mouse chirped, "Send the rabbit. He's the best runner."

Old Owl agreed. "He hops and skips well, and he is not selfish. He may catch the sun."

So the rabbit was sent on a trip of many days. At the bottom of the earth, he found a crack of light. He went through the crack, and there he saw a great ball of fire resting in a stone pot.

Rabbit got to the ball of fire, and as he took it through the crack, the evil spirits started chasing him. Rabbit ran as fast as he could. Just as the evil spirits were about to catch him, Rabbit kicked the

ball of fire into two pieces.

He kicked the smaller piece into the sky, where it became the moon. He kicked the larger piece into another part of the sky, where it became the sun.

The earth brightened so that the evil spirits had to hide. They were never seen again. All the birds and beasts of the north land sang to honor the rabbit who had saved the sun. ❖

Sample Folktale Questions

1. What kind of folktale is "How the Sun Was Saved"?
   A. fable
   B. myth
   C. legend
   D. fairy tale

2. How can you tell?

   _____

   _____

3. What does this story mainly teach?
   A. how strong and fast a rabbit is
   B. why we have a sun and a moon
   C. how to overcome evil in the world
   D. why some people are greedy and others are giving

Additional Practice Questions

4. Where does the story "How the Sun Was Saved" take place?
   A. in the city
   B. in the desert
   C. on an island
   D. in the north land

5. Which animal is first suggested as the one who should go get the sun?
   A. owl
   B. wolf
   C. rabbit
   D. polar bear

Seeing the Writer in the Writing

Behind every story, poem, article, or play is a writer (author) who wants to share something with you. Reading can be like listening to the writer talking to you in your mind. In this lesson, you will learn how to figure out just what the writer is trying to say to you.

Tip 1 **Find the speaker or narrator in the passage.**

While reading fiction, ask yourself this question: "Who is telling the story?" Sometimes the writer will have one of the characters tell the story. The character will talk about himself or herself using words such as "*I*," "*me*," or "*mine*." The following passage is an example of this kind of writing.

> I, Nate the Great, am a busy detective. One morning I was not busy. I was on vacation. I was sitting under a tree enjoying the breeze with my dog, Sludge, and a pancake.

—from *Nate the Great and the Lost List* by Marjorie Weinman Sharmat

Sometimes writers write about themselves. When writers write about themselves they are writing **autobiographies**. Read the following passage in which the writer, Helen Keller, tells about herself.

> As soon as I could spell a few words my teacher gave me slips of cardboard on which were printed words in raised letters.

—from *The Story of My Life* by Helen Keller

Sometimes a fiction writer will use a narrator who is not a part of the story. He or she may share the thoughts and feelings of all the characters with the reader. (These types of narrators don't mention themselves at all.) The following passage is an example of this kind of writing.

> The boy was trying to read aloud, for he could understand better if he heard the words. But now he stopped. He did not understand what it said; the words were too new and strange. He was sad.

—from *Sounder* by William H. Armstrong

Practice Activity 1: Identifying the Speaker

Directions: Read the passages, then decide who the speaker is.

> While Wilbur was being unloaded and taken out of his crate and into his new pigpen, crowds gathered to watch. They stared at the sign ZUCKERMAN'S FAMOUS PIG. Wilbur stared back and tried to look extra good. He was pleased with his new home. The pen was grassy, and it was shaded from the sun by a shed roof.

—from *Charlotte's Web*, by E.B. White

1. Who is the speaker?
   A. Wilbur
   B. Mr. Zuckerman
   C. a person in the crowd
   D. a narrator outside the story

> In September 1925, when I was just nine, I set out on the first great adventure of my life—boarding-school. My mother had chosen for me a Prep School in a part of England which was as near as it could possibly be to our home in South Wales, and it was called St. Peter's.

—from *Boy: Tales of Childhood* by Roald Dahl

2. Who is the speaker?
   A. a nine-year-old boy
   B. the writer's mother
   C. the writer, Roald Dahl
   D. a narrator outside the story

Jerry, take it easy, I warned myself. Maybe the latch is loose. Maybe the attic door always swings open. It's an old house, remember?

—from *Goosebumps: Piano Lessons Can Be Murder* by R.L. Stine

3. Who is the speaker?

   A. Jerry

   B. Jerry's friend

   C. the writer, R.L. Stine

   D. a narrator outside the story

Toad was asleep, and he was having a dream. He was on a stage, and he was wearing a costume. Toad looked out into the dark. Frog was sitting in the theater. A strange voice from far away said, "PRESENTING THE GREATEST TOAD IN ALL THE WORLD!"

—from *Frog and Toad Together* by Arnold Lobel

4. Who is the speaker?

   A. Toad

   B. Frog

   C. a strange voice

   D. a narrator outside the story

My brother had, in 1720 or 1721, begun to print a newspaper. It was the second that appeared in America, and was called the *New England Courant* . . . I was employed to carry the papers thro' the streets to the customers.

—from *The Autobiography of Benjamin Franklin*

5. Who is the speaker?

   A. a paper boy

   B. the writer's brother

   C. the writer, Benjamin Franklin

   D. a narrator outside the story

Tip 2 **Look for hints that tell you what the writer wants you to feel.**

When reading a scary story, you most likely will feel scared. When reading a story about Abraham Lincoln or Eleanor Roosevelt, you might feel interested or proud. There's a reason you have these feelings. In a scary story, the writer chooses scary words and phrases such as *dark and rainy night*, *as dry as dead leaves*, and *heavy, dragging footsteps*. In a story about Abraham Lincoln or Eleanor Roosevelt, the writer chooses words and phrases such as *powerful speaker*, *a symbol of hope for many people*, and *strong leader*.

Read the following sentences from *Sarah, Plain and Tall*, by Patricia MacLachlan. Pay close attention to the words and phrases the writer uses to hint at how she wants you to feel. Then answer the questions that follow.

> The rain came and passed, but strange clouds hung in the northwest, low and black and green. And the air grew still.

6. Which word best describes how the author wants readers to feel?
   A. silly
   B. angry
   C. happy
   D. worried

7. What are some words or phrases that tell you what the writer wants you to feel?

   _____

   _____

8. Now it's your turn. Make up a few sentences or a paragraph that you think will make your readers smile or laugh. Try to think of something silly or funny.

   _____

   _____

   _____

   _____

Tip 3 The theme (or author's message) connects the meaning of the story to the reader.

The main message of a story is called the **theme**. The theme is bigger than the main idea. It tells more than just who did what in the story. The theme connects the story to the reader and the reader's world. It may be an idea the author has about what people are like, such as "It isn't always easy for people to be patient."

Sometimes the theme is a lesson that the writer wants you to learn from the story, such as "It is always better to tell the truth than to lie." The lesson is sometimes called a **moral**.

Theme can be explained most easily by using examples. Read the following fable by Aesop.

The Travelers and the Tree
a fable by Aesop, retold by Eugene Gannon

Two travelers were worn out by the heat of a summer's day. At noon, they stopped to rest under a tall cottonwood tree.

As they lay in its shade, one traveler said to the other, "The cottonwood is certainly a useless tree! It doesn't grow fruit. And its wood is too soft to use for building houses. Why, it isn't even any good for burning in a fireplace!"

"You're right," said the other traveler. "This useless tree might as well blow down in the next storm, for all that it would matter to the world."

The cottonwood tree angrily shook its leaves above their heads. "How dare you lie in the coolness of my shade and yet call me useless!" it said. ❖

9. What lesson does the author want readers to learn from "The
   Travelers and the Tree"?
   A. Don't brag to others.
   B. Traveling can be very tiring.
   C. Cottonwood trees are not very useful.
   D. There is goodness and value in most things.

10. Think of a story that you've read in the last week or two. Can you
    describe it's theme?

    _____

    _____

    _____

    _____

⎯⎯⎯ Seeing the Writer in the Writing ⎯⎯⎯
Lesson 14 Review

When reading, always remember that a writer is behind
the writing. To do this, keep the following tips in mind:

- Find the speaker or narrator in the passage.

- Look for hints that tell you what the writer wants you
  to feel.

- The theme (or author's message) connects the
  meaning of the story to the reader.

Practice Passage

Directions: Read the passage and answer the questions that follow.

Life in the New World
by Mickey Toom

Life wasn't easy for the Blake family. They had come to America in 1640, twenty years after the first Pilgrims had arrived from England. Nine-year-old Charity and her parents left behind a comfortable home, fine clothes, and many friends. They also left behind their familiar city life to move to a strange and sometimes dangerous land far, far from home.

Here in the New World, the family worked together to build a rough cabin along a dirt trail. Charity's father had been a printer in London. He knew very little about building a house. But friendly neighbors helped the family build a one-room hut and cover it with a roof of grass. As men laid the logs in place, Charity and her mother filled the cracks with mud. The family cooked, ate, played, slept, and worked in that one dark room.

Neighbors taught Charity and her mother which berries to gather from the forest and the best ways to cook wild game and fowl. They also taught Charity's father how to hunt, fish, and plant crops. More and more everyday, the Blake family began to feel at home. ❖

Sample Author Questions

1. Who is the speaker in this passage?
   A. Charity Blake
   B. the Blake family
   C. the Blake's neighbors
   D. a narrator outside the story

2. Which word best describes how the author wants readers to feel about the Blake family?

   A. angry

   B. proud

   C. nervous

   D. miserable

3. What is the author's message in this story?

   A. Old friends are the best friends.

   B. Moving is sometimes a bad idea.

   C. All people should move far from home.

   D. Friends can help make hard times easier.

Additional Practice Questions

4. Charity's father knew little about building houses because

   A. he had never built one before.

   B. he preferred printing to house-building.

   C. Charity and her mother did most of that kind of work.

   D. his neighbors built all the houses while he did the printing.

5. Which of the following best describes why the Blake family began to feel at home?

   A. They cooked, ate, played, slept, and worked in a dark room.

   B. Their neighbors were helpful and everyone worked together.

   C. They left behind a comfortable home, fine clothes, and many friends.

   D. They came to America twenty years after the first Pilgrims arrived from England.

You Be the Editor

In Units 2 and 3, you read all kinds of writing—articles, directions, made-up stories, even poems. In Lesson 14, you learned how to see the writer in the writing. Now it's your turn to be the writer, as well as the editor, of your own writing.

Writers don't stop after they get their words on paper for the first time. They go back to revise and edit their writing to make it the best it can be.

Some writers have people who help them edit their work. These people are called editors. Editors help polish a writer's work until it "shines" and the writer's thoughts are as polished as a shiny apple. When you're done with Units 4 and 5, you'll be a good writer and editor, too!

In This Unit
◆ *Building Sentences*
◆ *Sentence Types and Punctuation*
◆ *Editing for Capitalization*

Lesson 15

Building Sentences

In Lesson 1, you learned that words come in parts, like building blocks. Sentences are a lot like building blocks, too. If you don't put them together properly, you can't build anything. But if you are careful in putting your words together, you can build great sentences.

Different kinds of words, such as subjects, verbs, nouns, and pronouns, are meant to fit together in certain ways. In this lesson, you'll learn how to make your sentences stick together like a sturdy castle made of building blocks.

Tip 1 **Every complete sentence has a subject and a predicate.**

A complete sentence must have both a subject and a predicate. Read the following sentence.

> Andy's hat flew out the window.

The **subject** is the word or group of words that the sentence is about. The subject of this sentence is *Andy's hat.*

The subject must always contain a noun. A **noun** is a word for a person, a place, or a thing. *Hat* is the noun in the subject of the example.

The **predicate** is the part of the sentence that tells what the subject is or does. The predicate of this sentence is *flew out the window.*

The predicate must always contain a verb. A **verb** is a word that tells what something is or does. *Flew* is the verb in the predicate of the example.

Practice Activity 1: Subjects and Predicates

Directions: Underline the subject of each sentence and circle the predicate.

Example: <u>Steve and Maria</u> (played softball at recess).

1. The fourth-grade class went on a field trip.

2. Your brother missed the bus.

3. The spaceship landed on the planet Mars.

4. My desk needs to be straightened.

5. Mr. Yang carried his books to the car.

Tip 2 Make subjects and verbs match.

Verbs must agree with their subjects. When you have a **singular** subject (one thing, such as a *puppy*, a *sock*, or a *movie*), that word takes a singular verb (such as *stinks*). Most singular verbs end in *s*. If you have a **plural** subject (more than one thing, such as *puppies*, *socks*, or *movies*), that word takes a plural verb (such as *stink*). Look at the following examples:

Singular	Plural
The onion *makes* my eyes water.	The onions *make* my eyes water.
The bug *jumps*.	The bugs *jump*.
This Japanese character *means* "happiness."	These Japanese characters *mean* "peaceful house."

Practice Activity 2: Subjects and Verbs

Directions: In the following sentences, circle the verb that matches the subject.

> **Example:** The birds in that birch tree (is /(are)) all blue jays.

6. *Mother Goose and Grimm* comics (make / makes) me fall over laughing.

7. A flock of geese (is / are) called a *gaggle*.

8. All of my cousins, except Cecil, (has / have) dark black hair.

9. Pineapples and kiwi fruit (is / are) both delicious with chocolate ice cream.

10. The fangs on that vampire (is / are) scary.

Tip 3 **Make nouns and pronouns match.**

Read the following sentences.

> The Johnsons wanted to go to the store. They did not know it was closed.

They and *it* in the example are pronouns. A **pronoun** is a word that takes the place of a noun.

A plural noun, such as *the Johnsons*, can be replaced with a plural pronoun, such as *they*. A singular noun, such as *store*, can be replaced with a singular pronoun, such as *it*.

Here are a few pronouns you might use in your writing:

Singular			**Plural**		
I	you	he/she/it	we	you	they
me	you	him/her/it	us	you	them
my	your	his/her/its	our	your	their
mine	yours	his/hers/its	ours	yours	theirs

Practice Activity 3: Nouns and Pronouns

Directions: In the following sentences, circle the pronoun that matches the noun.

    Example: Look at the blue jays! Aren't (it / (they)) lovely?

11. Bobby, Peter, and Cindy were hungry because (he / they) forgot to bring the picnic basket.

12. My brother and his best friend want to build a giant fort, but (he / they) don't have enough wood.

13. Jesi likes to play with (her / their) sixteen kittens. She just got two of them yesterday.

14. Zoe plays soccer with Carlos because (he / they) is a good sport.

15. The bakery sells (its / their) day-old bread for half price.

Tip 4 **Verb tenses show past, present, and future.**

    A verb's **tense** tells when the action happens. Verbs can tell what happened in the past, what is happening now, or what will happen in the future. It is important to make sure that the verbs you use are all in the right tense.

Past tense verbs tell about actions that have already happened.

        Yesterday, we *painted*. Or: Yesterday, we *were painting*.

Present tense verbs describe actions that are happening now.

        We *paint*. Or: We *are painting*.

Future tense verbs describe actions that will happen in the future.

        Tomorrow, we *will paint*. Or: Tomorrow, we *are going to paint*.

Practice Activity 4: Verb Tenses

Directions: In the following sentences, circle the correct verb.

> **Example:** Heidi used to like tennis the best, but now she
> ((likes) / liked / will like) soccer more than tennis.

16. E. J. (wins / won / will win) the wheelchair race last Saturday.

17. Last October we (have / had / will have) two inches of rain.

18. My sister (is / was / will be) 10 next year.

19. Jim (is / was / will be) eight before I was.

20. By next summer, Jana (is / was / will be) able to swim freestyle.

Tip 5 **Adjectives draw pictures for your readers.**

> **Adjectives** are words that describe nouns. When you put adjectives into your sentences, you help your reader get a better picture of what you are writing about.

The adjectives in the following sentences are in boldfaced type.

> The **quick brown** fox jumped over the **lazy** dog.

In this example, the adjectives *quick* and *brown* describe the fox. *Lazy* describes the dog.

> Theo's **baby** sister has **red** hair.

Theo's sister is a baby. Her hair is red.

> The **old brick** house on the corner has **broken** windows.

The house is old and made of brick. Its windows are broken.

Adjectives make reading (and writing) more fun.

Practice Activity 5: Adding Adjectives

Directions: Fill in the blanks with words that describe the nouns.

21. Ellie had a _____ birthday party.

22. The _____ rabbit ran under the house.

23. Michael got a _____ shirt at the store.

24. The _____ balloon popped with a _____ sound.

25. I sat in my _____ chair and read a _____ book.

Tip 6 **The words *a, an*, and *the* introduce nouns.**

The little words *a*, *an*, and *the* are used to introduce nouns. These words are called **articles**.

When you use *the*, you are talking about the only one of something. *The* describes "this" thing. *The book* means *this book*. *The tree* means *this tree*.

When you use *a* or *an*, you are talking about one thing out of many. *A* and *an* describe "any" thing. *A book* means *any book*. *An apple* means *any apple*. The word *a* is used before nouns that start with a consonant sound; the word *an* is used before words that begin with a vowel (*a, e, i, o, u*) sound.

Practice Activity 6: *A, An,* and *The*

Directions: Circle the word that fits best in the sentence.

26. We sat on (a / an / the) front porch of my house.

27. Chris took (a / an / the) orange and passed the rest of the box to Sam.

28. Mrs. Montez bought (a / an / the) new coat at the mall.

29. Every night, Luis takes (a / an / the) same dog for a walk.

30. California is (a / an / the) finest state in America.

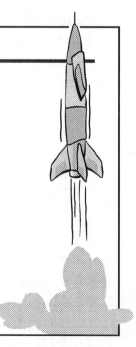

=== **Building Sentences** ===
Lesson 15 Review

When writing, remember the following tips:
- Every complete sentence has a subject and a predicate.
- Make subjects and verbs match.
- Make nouns and pronouns match.
- Verb tenses show past, present, and future.
- Adjectives draw pictures for your readers.
- The words *a, an,* and *the* introduce nouns.

Sample Building Sentences Questions

1. What is the best way to rewrite the underlined part of the following sentence?

   Last night, Farah's cat <u>jumps</u> out of the window.

   A. jump
   B. jumped
   C. will jump
   D. The sentence does not need to be rewritten.

2. What is the subject of the following sentence?

   Saturday, we played basketball.

   A. Saturday
   B. we
   C. played
   D. basketball

3. Which verb fits best in the following sentence?

   Right now, Ty _____ for the rain to stop.

   A. waited
   B. will wait
   C. is waiting
   D. was waiting

4. What is the best way to rewrite the underlined part of the following sentence?

   <u>Monkeys dreams</u> about driving cars.

   A. Monkey dreams
   B. Monkeys dream
   C. Monkey dream
   D. The sentence does not need to be rewritten.

5. Which pronoun fits best in the following sentence?

   Brad and his father built a tree house in _____ yard.

   A. its
   B. his
   C. her
   D. their

6. Read the following sentence.

   The monster ate the smelly socks in one bite.

   Which word is an adjective describing the word *socks*?

   A. monster
   B. smelly
   C. one
   D. bite

7. Which article fits best in the following sentence?

   Each morning, we pick out books in _____ school library.
   A. a
   B. an
   C. its
   D. the

8. Which verb fits best in the following sentence?

   The singer _____ not know the song very well.
   A. do
   B. does
   C. done
   D. will do

9. Which pronoun fits best in the following sentence?

   You should clean _____ room before Grandma gets here.
   A. your
   B. their
   C. them
   D. yours

10. Which article fits best in the following sentence?

    Joe DiMaggio had _____ special baseball bat.
    A. a
    B. an
    C. its
    D. the

Lesson 16

Sentence Types and Punctuation

"Is it still raining?"

"Yes, it is."

"Aww . . . we won't be able to play outside at recess!"

"Wear your boots."

You just read four different types of sentences. This lesson will show you the difference between sentence types and how to use them. It will also look at some special punctuation rules you need to know in third grade.

Tip 1 **Some sentences make statements.**

Many sentences make statements. They state a fact or tell a piece of information.

The sky is blue.

I am going home.

Twelve eggs make a dozen.

You can spot sentences like this by the way they stop. Statements end with a **period**.

On the following lines, write three statements of your own. Be sure they are complete sentences with a subject and a predicate.

1. _____

2. _____

3. _____

Tip 2 **Some sentences ask questions.**

If you want to know something, you ask a question.

Which way did she go?

Have you ever seen a purple cow?

Who drank all of the lemonade?

Questions always end with a **question mark**.

On the following lines, write three questions of your own. Be sure they are complete sentences with a subject and a predicate.

4. _____

5. _____

6. _____

Tip 3 **Some sentences get excited!**

Sometimes when you are excited about something, you shout. You might say something like, "Wow!" Sentences that show excitement end with an **exclamation point**.

We won the game!

I can't believe you ate the whole bunch of carrots!

I think we're having an earthquake!

On the following lines, write three sentences of your own that end with an exclamation point. Be sure they are complete sentences with a subject and a predicate.

7. _____

8. _____

9. _____

Tip 4 **Some sentences tell what to do.**

Look at the following sentences that tell what to do.

Come here.

Look at the stars.

Go to bed!

These sentences are called **commands**. They are different from most other sentences because the subject is understood. It's easier if you imagine the word *you* before each command sentence.

You come here.

You look at the stars.

You go to bed!

On the following lines, write three commands of your own. Don't write the word *you* in them. Write them so that *you* is understood.

10. <u>Go to bed.</u>

11. _____

12. _____

Punctuation

You just learned end punctuation for different types of sentences. Now let's review some other punctuation rules.

Tip 5 **Put a comma between the day and year when writing a date.**

When you write a date, put a comma between the day of the month and the year.

February 29, 2000

When you put a date into a sentence, put a comma after both the day of the month and the year.

On April 22, 1960, Kyoko's mother was born.

Tip 6 **Put a comma between the name of a city and its state.**

When you write the name of a city and a state, put a comma between them.

> Lodi, California

Use a comma even if you are not writing out the whole name of the state.

> I grew up in Stockton, CA.

When you write the name of a city and state, put a comma after both the city and the state.

> My friend Ernie lived in Frog Jump, Tennessee, until he was five years old.

> I went to Iowa City, Iowa, to visit relatives.

Tip 7 **Put commas between the street address, city, and state in an address when they are in a sentence.**

An address has the following parts:

- street address (2221 Forest Street)
- city (Long Beach)
- state (California)
- ZIP code (90801)

When you are writing an address in a sentence, put a comma between the street address, city, and state. Do not put a comma between the state and ZIP code.

> Fritz and Mary live at 2221 Forest Street, Long Beach, California 90801.

Practice Activity 1: Punctuation in Dates and Addresses

13. Write the month, day, and year on which you were born.

   _____

14. Write a complete sentence that has today's date in it. (Hint: It can start with "Today is . . .")

   _____

   _____

15. Write the name of a city and state you have visited.

   _____

16. Write a complete sentence that has your name and full address in it. (Hint: It can have the words, "My name is . . ." and "I live at . . .")

   _____

   _____

Tip 8 **When you list things in a sentence, put commas after each one except the last one.**

Read the following sentence.

> I went to the grocery store and bought milk eggs bread apples and rice.

What in the world are *milk eggs* and *bread apples*? This sentence doesn't make much sense. But if we put in some commas, it will.

> I went to the grocery store and bought milk, eggs, bread, apples, and rice.

Whenever you list things in a sentence, put commas after each item except the last one.

Rewrite the following sentences. Put commas where they belong.

17. Today I am going to read a book eat lunch take a nap and play
    with my dog.

    _____

    _____

18. Ryan Denise Christa and Trisha are learning to play the piano.

    _____

    _____

Book Titles

You read lots of books in school, so you need to know the special way
to write book titles.

Tip 9 **Book titles should be capitalized and underlined or written in italics.**

The first word of all important words in book titles should be in capital
letters. If you are using a computer, book titles are typed in **italics**,
which looks *like this*. The words *a, an, of, the, in, on,* and *at* are not
capitalized unless they are the first word of the title.

> *Charlotte's Web*
>
> *Where the Wild Things Are*
>
> *The Cat in the Hat*

When you are handwriting or using a typewriter, <u>underline</u> book
titles instead.

19. On the following lines, write the titles of two books you have read.

    _____

    _____

Sentence Types and Punctuation
Lesson 16 Review

Remember the following tips about sentence types and punctuation:

- Some sentences make statements.

- Some sentences ask questions.

- Some sentences get excited!

- Some sentences tell what to do.

- Put a comma between the day and the year when writing a date.

- Put a comma between the name of a city and its state.

- Put commas between the street address, city, and state in an address when they are in a sentence.

- When you list things in a sentence, put commas after each one except the last one.

- Book titles should be capitalized and underlined or written in italics.

Sample Sentence Types and Punctuation Questions

1. What is the correct way to rewrite the underlined part of the following address?

   Send your letter to the <u>Bartlett Family, 2144 Central Avenue Concord California, 94520</u>.
   A. Bartlett Family, 2144 Central Avenue, Concord California, 94520
   B. Bartlett Family 2144 Central Avenue, Concord, California, 94520
   C. Bartlett Family, 2144 Central Avenue, Concord, California 94520
   D. The underlined part does not need to be rewritten.

2. Which of the following dates is punctuated correctly?
   A. April 9 1865   C. April 9, 1865
   B. April, 9 1865   D. April, 9, 1865

3. Which book title is written correctly?
   A. *pinocchio*
   B. *Stuart little*
   C. *Black Beauty*
   D. *The little prince*

4. What is the correct way to punctuate the underlined part of the following sentence?

   <u>Hot dogs hamburgers chips and salsa</u> are on the menu for our picnic.
   A. Hot dogs hamburgers, chips and salsa
   B. Hot dogs, hamburgers chips and salsa
   C. Hot dogs, hamburgers, chips, and salsa
   D. Hot, dogs hamburgers, chips, and salsa

5. Which punctuation mark should come at the end of the following sentence?

   Where have you been _____
   A. .   C. !
   B. ,   D. ?

Editing for Capitalization

What if you read a paragraph that looked like this?

> *all i have Ever Wanted was A supER LooPdiDDLe SliDe. mY broTher rOnny waNted a Football, So He GoT a FootBall. MY CoUSin chASE Wanted a NEW Set of ColorED Pencils, SO he GoT A New SeT of COLOred PencIls. all i have EVER ASked foR iS OnE teenY, Tiny backYard Super LOOPdiddlE SliDE, and WHat Do I GET? a new Pair of OrANGE SockS!*

Besides thinking that the author *really really* wants a Super Loopdiddle Slide, you would also probably think, *What's going on here?* If there were no rules for capitalization, things could get pretty hard to read.

You may not think much about capitalization rules when you start writing. You can't forget them altogether, though. If your writing is capitalized in strange ways, it might be hard for others to read. And it might take them a long time to read it. They may not want to bother reading your writing at all.

Tip 1 Learn the editor's tools for capitalization.

Learning the editor's tools for capitalization will help you when you edit your writing. Look at the tools that follow, then read the examples. Notice how the marks are used to correct mistakes in capitalization.

> ≡ Make a capital letter.

jenny went to chuck's restaurant for her birthday.

> / Make a small letter.

I Ate raw carrot sticks and Peanut Butter for dinneR.

You will have a chance to use more editor's tools in Lesson 20.

Tip 2 **When editing, always check for capitalization.**

Below are some important rules to help you check for capitalization.

Always capitalize . . .

1. **the first word of each sentence.**

   <u>O</u>ur softball team is doing really well. <u>W</u>e won a game last month.

2. **people's names.**

<u>J</u>ulia <u>C</u>hild	<u>I</u>sadora <u>D</u>uncan	<u>I</u>samu <u>N</u>ogushi
<u>R</u>obert <u>F</u>rost	<u>S</u>ally <u>K</u>. <u>R</u>ide	my cousin <u>H</u>arriet

3. **titles that go with people's names.**

<u>P</u>rince <u>P</u>hillip	<u>S</u>enator <u>M</u>ack	<u>D</u>r. <u>J</u>ones
<u>P</u>resident <u>C</u>linton	<u>G</u>eneral <u>S</u>tillwell	<u>A</u>untie <u>E</u>m

4. **family titles used in place of names.**

<u>M</u>om	<u>D</u>ad	<u>G</u>randfather	<u>G</u>randma

   But, write *John's* (m)om; *my* (d)ad; *her* (g)randfather; *their* (g)randma. When titles like these are used, they show the person's relationship, but they are not being used in place of the person's given name.

5. **geographical names including: cities, states, countries, continents, and languages.**

<u>A</u>lameda	<u>C</u>anada	<u>A</u>sian
<u>C</u>alifornia	<u>E</u>nglish	<u>D</u>utch

6. **days, months, holidays, historical periods, and special events. Do NOT capitalize seasons.**

   <u>S</u>aturday, <u>J</u>uly 4, is <u>I</u>ndependence <u>D</u>ay. It is just one of many summer holidays.

   The Flintstones are supposed to be from the <u>S</u>tone <u>A</u>ge.

7. **brand names.**

<u>F</u>ruit <u>L</u>oops	<u>H</u>ot <u>W</u>heels
<u>M</u>ountain <u>D</u>ew	<u>S</u>ega <u>D</u>reamcast

8. **titles of books, movies, and songs. Do NOT capitalize words such as *of*, *and*, or *the* unless they are the first word of the title.**

The <u>W</u>izard (o)f *<u>O</u>z*	*Little <u>H</u>ouse* (o)n (t)he *<u>P</u>rairie*
<u>T</u>arzan	"<u>T</u>hree <u>B</u>lind <u>M</u>ice"

9. **the word *I*.**

   Ananda and <u>I</u> look much different with our noses smushed up against the car windows.

Practice Activity 1: Editing for Capitalization

Directions: Proofread the following sentences. Use the editor's mark for capitalization (≡) below each letter that should be capitalized. Then rewrite each sentence using proper capitals. You may look back at the rules on page 124 for help.

1. have you read *the boxcar children*, a book by gertrude chandler warner?

   _____

   _____

2. my cousin mary jo from canada speaks two languages: french and english.

   _____

   _____

3. on monday, january 18, our country will celebrate martin luther king, jr. day.

   _____

   _____

4. this friday, carlos and i are planning to watch the movie *toy story 2*.

   _____

   _____

5. when did the boston tea party take place?

   _____

   _____

Practice Activity 2: Capitalization

Directions: Read the following sentences and select the word needing capitalization. If the capitalization in the sentence is correct, circle the letter D, "no mistake."

6. Last year, Mom, Dad, my sister loretta, and I moved from Scranton, Pennsylvania, to Berkeley, California.

   A. Year   C. Loretta

   B. Sister   D. no mistake

7. Californians come from many different cultural backgrounds, including mexican, Chinese, Japanese, and Native American.

   A. Cultural   C. Mexican

   B. Backgrounds   D. no mistake

8. My dad and I searched all day long for a Mother's day gift for Mom.

   A. Dad   C. Gift

   B. Day   D. no mistake

9. On her trip to South Dakota, Sarah saw Mount Rushmore, which features the faces of four presidents carved in stone.

   A. Trip   C. Presidents

   B. Four   D. no mistake

10. Elija, Tina, and my cousin Rey know how to speak spanish.

    A. My   C. Spanish

    B. Cousin   D. no mistake

Editing for Capitalization
Lesson 17 Review

When editing for capitalization, remember these tips:

- Learn the editor's tools for capitalization.
- When editing, always check for capitalization.

UNIT 5

Writing Tips

When writers put their fingers to the keyboard or grab a pencil to begin a story, they know that their writing will go through many steps before it's finished. These steps are: prewriting, writing, improving, and fixing mistakes.

In this unit, you will learn how to **prewrite**, or how to get ideas for your writing. You will write your sentences and put them into paragraphs. You will learn how to improve and **edit** (fix mistakes) in your writing, too. All of these steps are important parts of writing.

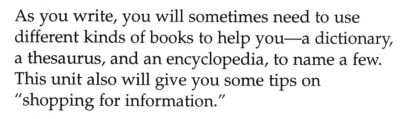

As you write, you will sometimes need to use different kinds of books to help you—a dictionary, a thesaurus, and an encyclopedia, to name a few. This unit also will give you some tips on "shopping for information."

In This Unit
- Getting Ideas
- Sentences Build Paragraphs
- Improving What You Have Written
- Shopping for Information

Lesson 18

Getting Ideas

Sometimes when you are told to write something, you know just what to write about. You can jump in and start putting your ideas together. Other times, you might sit and think and think and think—and still not feel like you have a good idea. What can you do then? This lesson will give you tips for getting writing ideas.

Tip 1 **Draw a picture to get ideas.**

Here's a fun way to get writing ideas: Draw them! Sometimes drawing a picture will help you think of ideas and details to write about.

1. Imagine that you are going to write about your favorite make-believe activity. Maybe you have built a fort and pretended it was a castle. Or maybe you like to play school with your little brother or sister. Think of as many make-believe activities as you can.

    In the following box, draw a picture of some of your favorite make-believe activities.

My Favorite Make-Believe Activities

Tell something about your drawing.

_____

_____

Tip 2 **Write about something you care about.**

If you are having trouble choosing an idea, ask yourself "Which idea am I most interested in?" or "Which thing do I know the most about?" Writers usually do their best when they write about something they care a lot about and know a lot about.

2. Which make-believe activity from your drawings in Number 1 do you think would help you do your best writing?

_____

Write one sentence telling why you think this idea is the best choice.

_____

_____

Tip 3 **Use your five senses to get ideas.**

Another way to get ideas is to close your eyes for a minute and imagine yourself in the middle of whatever you are writing about. Wait—don't close your eyes yet! Remember that your five senses are sight, hearing, smell, taste, and touch. When you close your eyes, try to imagine things you would *see, hear, smell, taste,* and *feel* if you were in the middle of what you are writing about.

3. Okay, now close your eyes for a minute and think about your topic with all five senses.

Once you've spent a little time thinking, write your ideas in the table.

My Make-Believe Activity	
Things I saw	
Things I heard	
Things I smelled	
Things I tasted	
Things I felt	
Things I did	
Other things: (place, time, and so on)	

Tip 4 **Have a thinking storm in your mind.**

Suppose you still feel stuck. Try brainstorming! **Brainstorming** is a word for writing down everything that pops into your mind. Don't let your pencil stop moving, and don't worry about whether your ideas are good or bad. Write clearly enough that you can read your writing later, but don't worry about poor spelling, sloppy writing, or punctuation. Just be sure to get your storm of words down on paper.

Isabel brainstormed about her make-believe activity: living in a house made out of clouds. After you look over this brainstorming, do the brainstorming activity on the next page to put together ideas and details about *your* make-believe activity.

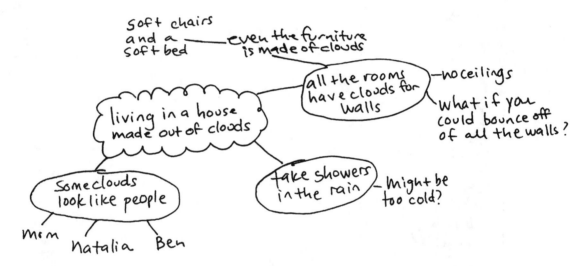

4. Brainstorm ideas and details about your make-believe activity in the storm cloud below. Once you begin writing, don't put down your pencil until the cloud is full. Don't worry about complete sentences or spelling. Don't even worry about what your writing looks like. Just make sure you can read it when you are done.

Getting Ideas
Lesson 18 Review

The next time you need a writing idea, try a few of the prewriting tips you practiced in this lesson:

- Draw a picture to get ideas.

- Choose a topic you care about.

- Use your five senses to get ideas.

- Have a thinking storm in your mind.

Lesson 19

Sentences Build Paragraphs

A **paragraph** is a group of sentences about the same thing. All of the sentences in a paragraph should be about one main idea. If any of the sentences are about another idea, they belong in a new paragraph.

Think of the way the same kinds of foods are grouped together in a grocery store. All of the fruit is put in one place, all of the bread in another, and so on. If everything was mixed together on different shelves, it would be hard for people to find what they need. In the same way, it would be hard for people to read your writing if you mixed all your ideas together.

Here are some tips that will help you group your sentences into paragraphs.

Tip 1 The topic (main idea) sentence tells what a paragraph is about.

The most important part of a paragraph is the **topic sentence**. It tells the main idea of the paragraph. It is usually, but not always, the first sentence of the paragraph. Here's an example:

> I always enjoy visiting my grandmother's house.

Tip 2 The rest of the paragraph tells about the main idea of the topic sentence.

The topic sentence will be followed by ideas that explain or describe the main idea. For example, the topic sentence above will be followed by details about visiting Grandmother's house and *why* the writer enjoys those visits. The paragraph might read something like this:

> I always enjoy visiting my grandmother's house. I especially like to visit her kitchen. Grandmother bakes all kinds of good things to eat, and she always lets me test them. Sometimes I test so many cookies and brownies that I don't want to "test" my dinner.

Tip 3 A new idea gets a new paragraph.

When you are ready to discuss a new idea, begin a new paragraph.

> Another place I like to visit is Aunt Clara's condo. I don't bother going to her kitchen, though. She's never there. Aunt Clara hates to cook. This is no wonder because she is very bad at it. Aunt Clara is much better at playing video games. She has a whole library full of them!

The sentences about Aunt Clara wouldn't really fit in the paragraph about Grandmother. Aunt Clara needs a paragraph of her own.

Practice Activity: Writing a Paragraph

Directions: Write a short paragraph about a visit you enjoyed. Make sure your paragraph contains a topic sentence. Also, make sure all of the other sentences in your paragraph are about the main idea of the topic sentence. Include plenty of details to support your topic sentence.

_____

_____

_____

_____

_____

_____

_____

_____

_____

_____

_____

_____

_____

_____

_____

_____

_____

_____

_____

_____

_____

_____

_____

_____

Sentences Build Paragraphs
Lesson 19 Review

When writing paragraphs, remember the following tips:

- The topic (main idea) sentence tells what a paragraph is about.

- The rest of the paragraph tells about the main idea of the topic sentence.

- A new idea gets a new paragraph.

Lesson 20

Improving What You Have Written

Revising (improving) your writing is a lot like putting the final touches on an art project. Imagine you've started a painting of a leopard. First, you painted the tan coat. Now it's time to go back and add the black spots. You might decide to repaint one of the paws. You might also decide to add some grass and twisty trees. You might even fix the places where your paint ran when you hung it up to dry. After some reworking, your leopard looks great. But it didn't take just one step; it took many steps—just like good writing.

Tip 1 It's okay to make changes in your work.

Like painters, the best writers make changes to their work. Some writers make changes as they are writing. Others go back and make changes after they are all done. It is okay to erase or cross out as long as your changes are made neatly. You may want to use some of the symbols editors use when revising their first (rough) drafts.

Here's an example:

california become the thirty-first State on the September 9 1850.

Look at the first word in the sentence above: *california*. Following is the mark the editor used to show that the "c" should be capitalized.

> ☰ Make a capital letter.

Now look back to the word *State*. Following is the mark the editor used to show that the "S" should be a small letter "s."

> / Make a small letter.

To take something out, such as the word *the*, use this symbol:

> ℐ Take something out.

And to put something in, such as the comma after the date, use this symbol:

> ∧ Put something in.

Tip 2 **Make sure your writing is neat enough for others to read.**

Your readers won't know whether they like your writing if they can't read it. Your final copy should be neat enough for others to read easily. You may want to write in cursive, or you may want to print. Either is okay.

Practice Activity: Revising Your Writing

Directions: Read the following paragraph. Use the editors' symbols to make the changes that are needed.

Camels are Desert animals that can go for weaks

without food or water. The hump on a a camel's

bak is like a built-in food supply. unlike many people

think, the hump is not filled with Water. It is actually

a lump of fat that gives the camell energy when food

and water are hard to find If a camel goes too long

without eating or and drinking, its hump shrinks or

falls down on its side. after the camel rests and eats

again, the hump grow back two normal.

Tip 3 Use a checklist to revise your writing.

Checklists can be very helpful when you revise your writing. The following editor's checklist will help you plan your writing and check your work when you are finished.

The Editor's Checklist

My writing should follow these rules:

❑ Be clear and be supported with details.

❑ Have a clear beginning, middle, and end.

❑ Have correct spelling, end punctuation, and beginning capitalization.

❑ Have paragraphs for each new idea that begin and end in the right places.

❑ Be easy to read and show that I really care about my topic.

❑ Use clear and interesting words.

❑ Have different kinds of sentences that fit together and sound good when read aloud.

Improving What You Have Written
Lesson 20 Review

When revising your writing, remember the following tips:

• It's okay to make changes in your work.

• Make sure your writing is neat enough for others to read.

• Use a checklist to revise your writing.

Lesson 21

Shopping for Information

A supermarket has all kinds of foods and drinks, plus toothpaste, medicine, laundry soap, hand soap, dish soap (lots of soap!), and many other things your family needs. Each department is set up with a certain kind of food or product so you can find things more easily. Do you need bread? Go to the bread aisle. Do you need milk? There's the dairy case.

Even though you don't need a grocery cart, finding information in a library is a lot like going to a supermarket. Everything you need is there. You just need to know where to find it. (And the best part is that it's free!)

The tips in this lesson will tell you how to go shopping for information and what resources to use in order to find what you're looking for.

Tip 1 Know your ABCs.

Sure you already know your ABCs. But how quickly can you look up a word in a dictionary? Sometimes it might seem like a long time. That's because a dictionary alphabetizes words beginning with the first letter (**a**), then the second letter (**am**), then the third (**ami**), fourth (**amig**), and fifth (**amigo**), and so on. Look at the following list of words in alphabetical order.

      aloha

      amber

      amid

      amigo

Now does it make sense, amigo?

Practice Activity: Know Your ABCs

Directions: Put the following word lists in alphabetical order.

1. arm, dog, cat, egg, black

_____ _____ _____ _____ _____

2. hand, happy, grab, hall, gym

_____ _____ _____ _____ _____

3. tangle, theater, tale, treasure, tortoise

_____ _____ _____ _____ _____

Tip 2 A dictionary will help you learn new words.

Imagine you are busily reading when you come upon a word you don't know. It's time to go shopping for information. The best place to look for a new word is in a dictionary.

As you saw in Lesson 5, a **dictionary** is a list of words in alphabetical order. Each entry shows the word and tells you its meaning and how the word is pronounced. Sometimes a dictionary will show the word as it is used in a sentence.

Look at this example of a dictionary entry:

> **hot** (hawt) *adj.* **1. a:** having a high temperature **b:** having heat (It's a *hot* day.)

Tip 3 A thesaurus lists words with the same meaning.

Like a dictionary, a **thesaurus** is a list of words in alphabetical order. But instead of telling you what each word means, a thesaurus gives several other words that mean the same thing.

For example, you might be writing a report about the hottest place in the United States, Death Valley, California. You might want to use other words that mean the same as *hot*. If you looked up *hot* in a thesaurus, you would find words like *baking, blistering, boiling, burning, fiery, heated, scalding, scorching,* and *sizzling*.

4. Use a thesaurus to find three words that have the same meaning as the word *cold*. Write them on the lines below.

_____

_____

_____

Tip 4 **An atlas is a book of maps.**

If you need to find out where a city, mountain, lake, or other place is, you can shop for information in an atlas.

Atlases show counties, states, and countries. They also show oceans, lakes, rivers, mountains, and deserts. They often tell how many people live in a city, county, state, or nation. Some atlases contain maps of the entire world. Other atlases have maps of only one area, such as the *Atlas of North America*.

If your family takes a car trip across the country, the driver might use an atlas such as *The Rand McNally Road Atlas*. A road atlas gives a map for each state. The maps show the roads, highways, towns, and other information a driver needs.

> **Finding Information**
>
> You have probably looked up information in a book, magazine, or encyclopedia. You may have even talked to people or watched TV programs to get information for a report.
>
> But don't forget about using a computer. Your school's library may have an encyclopedia program on its computer. And the Internet can take you all over the world; you won't even need to leave your chair.

5. If you wanted to take a car trip from Sacramento, California, to Dallas, Texas, which of the following books would help you get there?
   A. *A Photo History of Dallas*
   B. *The Road Atlas of the United States*
   C. *Cars and Trucks and Things That Go*
   D. *Seeing California by Automobile*

Tip 5 **An encyclopedia tells a little bit about almost everything.**

Your library probably has several different sets of encyclopedias. An encyclopedia has articles on many subjects. A set of encyclopedias looks something like this:

The articles are arranged in alphabetical order by subject. If you wanted to learn about dinosaurs, you would look in Volume 2. It contains subjects beginning with the letters *D* (like "dinosaur"), *E*, and *F*.

6. In which encyclopedia volume would you expect to find an article about the Pacific Ocean?

   A. Volume 4

   B. Volume 5

   C. Volume 6

   D. Volume 7

═══════ **Shopping for Information** ═══════

Lesson 21 Review

• Know your ABCs.

• A dictionary will help you learn new words.

• A thesaurus lists words with the same meaning.

• An atlas is a book of maps.

• An encyclopedia tells a little bit about almost everything.

Sample Resource Questions

1. Which word list is in alphabetical order?

   A. medicine, moccasin, mystery, magician, mumble

   B. medicine, magician, mumble, mystery, moccasin

   C. magician, medicine, mumble, moccasin, mystery

   D. magician, medicine, moccasin, mumble, mystery

Directions: For the following questions, choose the type of resource that is most likely to contain the answer.

2. What river flows between California and Arizona?

   A. atlas   C. dictionary

   B. thesaurus   D. encyclopedia

3. What are the parts of a flower called?

   A. atlas

   B. thesaurus

   C. dictionary

   D. encyclopedia

4. What does it mean to *braise* something?

   A. atlas   C. dictionary

   B. thesaurus   D. encyclopedia

5. What is another word for *run*?

   A. atlas

   B. thesaurus

   C. dictionary

   D. encyclopedia

6. When did astronauts land on the moon?

   A. atlas

   B. thesaurus

   C. dictionary

   D. encyclopedia

Appendix

145

Spelling Log

Most of us are not terrible spellers. We just misspell the same words over and over.

Keeping a spelling log will help you improve your spelling. Any time your teacher points out a misspelled word in your work, record the correct spelling in this log. Then spell the word correctly four times. This will help you remember how to spell the word right the next time.

Correct Spelling _____

_____   _____

_____   _____

Correct Spelling _____

_____   _____

_____   _____

Correct Spelling _____

_____   _____

_____   _____

Correct Spelling _____

_____   _____

_____   _____

Correct Spelling _____

_____   _____

_____

Correct Spelling _____

_____ _____

_____ _____

Correct Spelling _____

_____ _____

_____ _____

Correct Spelling _____

_____ _____

_____ _____

Correct Spelling _____

_____ _____

_____ _____

Correct Spelling _____

_____ _____

_____ _____

Correct Spelling _____

_____ _____

_____ _____

Correct Spelling _____

_____ _____

_____ _____

Correct Spelling _____

_____   _____

_____   _____

Correct Spelling _____

_____   _____

_____   _____

Correct Spelling _____

_____   _____

_____   _____

Correct Spelling _____

_____   _____

_____   _____

Correct Spelling _____

_____   _____

_____   _____

Correct Spelling _____

_____   _____

_____   _____

Correct Spelling _____

_____   _____

_____   _____

Correct Spelling _____

_____   _____

_____   _____

Correct Spelling _____

_____   _____

_____   _____

Correct Spelling _____

_____   _____

_____   _____

Correct Spelling _____

_____   _____

_____   _____

Correct Spelling _____

_____   _____

_____   _____

Correct Spelling _____

_____   _____

_____   _____

Correct Spelling _____

_____   _____

_____   _____

Correct Spelling _____

_____ _____

_____ _____

Correct Spelling _____

_____ _____

_____ _____

Correct Spelling _____

_____ _____

_____ _____

Correct Spelling _____

_____ _____

_____ _____

Correct Spelling _____

_____ _____

_____ _____

Correct Spelling _____

_____ _____

_____ _____

Correct Spelling _____

_____ _____

_____ _____

English Language Arts Content Standards for California Public Schools, Grade 3

Blast Off on California English Language Arts, Book 3, is based on the following reading and writing content standards adopted by the California State Board of Education. The following table matches the standards with the *Blast Off* lessons in which they are addressed.

Grade 3 Reading

Standards	*Blast Off* Lesson(s)
1.0 Word Analysis and Vocabulary Development: Students . . . select and know how to translate letter patterns into spoken language using phonics, syllabication, and word parts.	
1.1 **Decoding and Word Recognition:** know and use complex word families when reading (e.g., -ight) to decode unfamiliar words	2
1.2 **Decoding and Word Recognition:** decode regular multi-syllable words	All
1.3 **Decoding and Word Recognition:** read narrative and expository text aloud with fluency and accuracy and with appropriate pacing, intonation, and expression	Optional for All Lessons
1.4 **Vocabulary and Concept Development:** use knowledge of antonyms, synonyms, homophones, and homographs to determine meaning of words	4
1.5 **Vocabulary and Concept Development:** demonstrate knowledge of levels of specificity among grade-appropriate words and explain the importance of these relations (e.g., dog/mammal/animal/living things)	5
1.6 **Vocabulary and Concept Development:** use sentence and word context to find meaning of unknown words	4, 5
1.7 **Vocabulary and Concept Development:** use a dictionary to learn the meaning and other features of unknown words	4, 5
1.8 **Vocabulary and Concept Development:** use knowledge of prefixes (e.g., un-, re-, pre-, bi-, mis-, dis-) and suffixes (e.g., -er, -est, -ful) to determine meaning of words	1

Grade 3 Reading *(Continued)*

Standards	Blast Off Lesson(s)
2.0 Reading Comprehension: Students read and understand grade-level-appropriate material. They draw upon a variety of comprehension strategies as needed, including generating and responding to essential questions, making predictions, and comparing information from several sources.	
2.1 **Structural Features of Informational Materials:** use titles, table of contents, chapter headings, glossaries and indexes to locate information in text	9
2.2 **Comprehension and Analysis of Grade-Level-Appropriate Text:** ask questions and support answers by connecting prior knowledge with literal and inferential information found in text	8
2.3 **Comprehension and Analysis of Grade-Level-Appropriate Text:** demonstrate comprehension by identifying answers in text	All
2.4 **Comprehension and Analysis of Grade-Level-Appropriate Text:** recall major points in text, and make and modify predictions about forthcoming information	7
2.5 **Comprehension and Analysis of Grade-Level-Appropriate Text:** distinguish between main idea and supporting details in expository text	6, 8
2.6 **Comprehension and Analysis of Grade-Level-Appropriate Text:** extract appropriate and significant information from text, including problems and solutions	7
2.7 **Comprehension and Analysis of Grade-Level-Appropriate Text:** follow simple multiple-step written instructions (e.g., how to assemble a product or use a game board)	10
3.0 Literary Response and Analysis: Students read and respond to a wide variety of significant works of children's literature. They distinguish between the structural features of text and the literary terms or elements (i.e., theme, plot, setting, and characters).	
3.1 **Structural Features of Literature:** distinguish among common forms of literature (e.g., poetry, drama, fiction, non-fiction)	11, 12
3.2 **Narrative Analysis of Grade-Level-Appropriate Text:** comprehend basic plots of classic fairy tales, myths, folktales, legends, and fables from around the world	13
3.3 **Narrative Analysis of Grade-Level-Appropriate Text:** determine what characters are like by what they say or do and by how the author or illustrator portrays them	11
3.4 **Narrative Analysis of Grade-Level-Appropriate Text:** determine the underlying theme or author's message in fictional and non-fiction text	13, 14
3.5 **Narrative Analysis of Grade-Level-Appropriate Text:** recognize the similarities of sounds in words and rhythmical patterns in a selection (e.g., onomatopoeia, alliteration)	12
3.6 **Narrative Analysis of Grade-Level-Appropriate Text:** identify the speaker or narrator in a selection	14

Grade 3 Writing

Standards	Blast Off Lesson(s)
1.0 Written . . . English Language Conventions: Students write . . . with a command of standard English conventions that are appropriate to each grade level.	
1.1 **Sentence Structure:** understand and be able to use complete and correct declarative, interrogative, imperative, and exclamatory sentences in writing and speaking	15, 16
1.2 **Grammar:** identify and use subject/verb agreement, pronouns, adjectives, compound words, and articles in writing and speaking	15
1.3 **Grammar:** use past, present, and future verb tenses in writing and speaking	15
1.4 **Grammar:** identify and use subject and predicate of single-clause sentences in writing and speaking	15
1.5 **Punctuation:** punctuate dates, city and state, and titles of books correctly	16
1.6 **Punctuation:** use commas in series, dates, locations, and addresses	16
1.7 **Capitalization:** capitalize geographical names, holidays, historical periods, and special events correctly	17
1.8 **Spelling:** spell correctly one-syllable words with blends, contractions, compounds, and orthographic patterns (e.g., qu, consonant doubling, change y to i) and common homophones (e.g., hair/hare)	2, 3
1.9 **Spelling:** arrange words in alphabetical order	21
1.0 Writing Strategies: Students write clear and coherent sentences and paragraphs that develop a central idea. Their writing considers audience and purpose. They successfully use the stages of the writing process (i.e., pre-writing, drafting, revising, and editing successive versions).	
1.1 **Organization and Focus:** create a single paragraph that 1) develops a topic sentence 2) includes simple supporting facts and details	19
1.2 **Penmanship:** write legibly in cursive or joined italic, adhering to margins and correct spacing between letters in a word and words in a sentence	Optional for All Lessons
1.3 **Research and Technology:** understand the structure, organization, and use of various reference materials (e.g., dictionary, thesaurus, atlas, encyclopedia)	21
1.6 **Revising and Evaluating Strategies:** revise drafts to improve the coherence and the logical progression of ideas, using an established rubric	20